Immunisation research: a summary volume

Volume 3
Edited by Valerie Hey

Social Science Research Unit
Institute of Education
University of London
18 Woburn Square
London WC1H 0NS

ACKNOWLEDGEMENTS

This immunisation review owes much to the many people whose hard work and help have made it possible. We are very grateful to Dr David Salisbury and Nick Adkin at the Department of Health for their advice, guidance and input; to Plain English Campaign for their contributions; to the reviewers; and to the Health Education Authority's Immunisation Team who have all given their full support.

Health Education Authority
Trevelyan House
30 Great Peter Street
London
SW1P 2HW

Printed in England
ISBN 0 7521 0645 7

Contents

Foreword

Ten years ago, immunisation coverage in this country was amongst the lowest third of European countries. Measles epidemics were common with as many as 100,000 reported cases and up to 20 deaths in any one year. Now, coverage is amongst the highest in Europe. New vaccines have been introduced, for example Hib vaccine, with the virtual disappearance of the invasive infections caused by that organism. Epidemics are anticipated and prevented. As we go into the twenty-first century, we can look forward to the global eradication of poliomyelitis, the successful achievement of which will mean that we no longer need to immunise our children against that disease. Measles eradication might follow and, with the rapid advances in molecular biology, we can expect new and improved vaccines against infectious and non-infectious diseases.

Whilst there have been considerable operational and technical improvements in immunisation over the last decade, we depend on committed and informed health professionals providing an outstanding service to parents and children. For that service to be most effective, health professionals need to be able to counsel parents in a way that is informative without being patronising, clear and concise, yet taking account of the complex issues that are involved. They must be eloquent in conveying the outstanding personal benefit that children gain through being immunised and the infinitesimally small risks that are attached. In order to undertake this task, health professionals need to understand the tensions that parents face in coming to their decisions. These three volumes provide a detailed account that helps in understanding the factors that contribute to that decision-making process, ranging from the sources of information that are available to parents, to a full enquiry into the circumstances that have contributed to the decisions of a small, but vocal, part of the community to decline immunisation for their children. Within these volumes, the reader will achieve further insight into the interplay between health professional and parent. There will be many important messages.

Those health professionals working in immunisation have much for which they can be rightly proud. With their contribution, we have one of the leading immunisation programmes in the world. Nonetheless, we cannot afford to be complacent and must continually question if the service that we provide is the best possible. The material in these volumes will assist in that task.

DR D M SALISBURY MB BS FRCPCH MFPHM
Head, Immunisation and Infectious Diseases Group
Department of Health, London

Introduction

The Health Education Authority (HEA) has an educational remit in relation to both parents and health professionals. For this dual purpose to be effective, the HEA has to reconcile its awareness of individual, family and cultural diversity with a strategic concern for promoting the 'health of the nation'.[1] Previous work has already identified the challenges involved in transforming health behaviours.[2] Changing individual behaviour, whether the focus is upon stopping smoking[3] or in securing a high uptake of early childhood immunisation[4], is not straightforward.

Whilst childhood immunisation is a central public health issue, the immunisation decision is one of the first crucial 'private' health decisions that each parent makes. Information about factors that underlie parents' respective decisions is important to strategists and service providers. It is quite clear from the following studies that, where parents judge the quality of immunisation services negatively, they are less likely to comply with the immunisation programme.[4] In view of professional commitment to childhood immunisation, there is clearly a need to provide health professionals with material which outlines current research understandings about parents' views and experiences.

Taken from the perspective of parents, early childhood immunisation is mainly experienced as a private matter[5] and its attendant and inescapable risks in relation to an individual child can be calculated. One abiding theme is the dilemma experienced by mothers in reconciling their responsibility of care to an individual child with pressures exerted by professionals in their role as the guardians of public health. Others also, most notably general practitioners (GPs), are not immune to the contradictory nature of their role as both public health care professionals and family doctors.[6]

Generally, coverage rates in England and Wales have improved to the extent that the prevalence of childhood infectious diseases has declined substantially.[7] However, various studies demonstrate that the re-emergence of infectious disease has invariably followed a decline in coverage rates. The incidence of whooping cough in the late 1970s and early 1980s in England and Wales[8] was a case in point. The HEA has understandably concentrated its attention on sustaining high coverage rates to support the 95% targets set by the Department of Health (DoH).[9] Particular concerns centre on 'pockets of low cover', often disguised by global figures.[10] Gill and Sutton make a case for more precise, geographic- or location-specific health education targeting (1998).[4]

In order to discover the current factors involved in low uptake of early childhood immunisation, the HEA commissioned a sequence of reports which investigated both the delivery and reception of aspects of the childhood immunisation programme. The research reported here, covered:

- parental attitudes in respect of immunisation uptake;[4,5]
- professionals' beliefs and experiences;[11]
- the specific health education needs of professionals;[6]
- factors associated with the low uptake of immunisation focusing upon the role of health education initiatives.[12]

In seeking out such a broad range of opinion, the HEA explicitly provided an opportunity for the emergence of differing and shared viewpoints. The following statement captures the HEA position:

> *The HEA intends to establish the notion that the partnership between health professionals and parents should be one based on mutual trust and respect. This can only become a reality if professionals respect parents' wishes, are able to elicit and respond to their fears and beliefs and, within a supportive relationship, enable them to make an informed choice about immunisation.*[7]

This volume draws upon two related comprehensive literature reviews,[7,13] but has a narrower pragmatic purpose: it provides some key findings about the beliefs, attitudes and practices of parents and professionals. This brief sequence of summaries necessarily omits a great deal of information as its focus is to bring to the fore two central sets of related questions. First, what are the different perspectives of the various immunisation 'stakeholders'? Second, what are the differing information needs of parents and professionals? The format of the document sets concise summaries of each research study within an appropriate context by describing the study's methodological framework, detailing the research emphasis and specifying the core findings.

The HEA has increasingly recognised the impact of people's familial and social circumstances on their responses to health interventions. Important work has looked at how families talk and mediate health messages.[2,14] This body of work has shown that parental information needs are dynamic and change according to life stage. Likewise, the education needs of professionals are subject to development and alteration.

Interestingly, both findings are replicated in the childhood immunisation research programme. Professionals expressed concern that they were not forewarned about policy changes to the administration of MMR (measles, mumps, rubella).[11] Additionally, service providers specifically requested information designed to counter what they saw as the excessively one-sided views of certain popular broadcast and journalist media. These 'scare stories' feed professional demands to 'keep ahead of the game' and point to complex sociological questions about the increase in public scepticism regarding orthodox medicine. The proliferation of knowledge about health and health maintenance is worthy of greater empirical investigation.[4]

In addition to raising a number of practical points about the field of early childhood immunisation, this volume suggests a need to keep in mind more theoretical questions about the social meaning of health and health management in late modern society.[5] Others have called for an explicit recognition of 'conflicting values' [as] integral to discussion of childhood immunisation'.[6] If we understand health behaviour and practices within a context of debates about risk and difference, we can better appreciate the complex task that confronts health educators and parents alike.

References

1. Department of Health. *The Health of the Nation: a consultative document for health in England*. 1992. Cm1523. HMSO, London.

2. Holland, J., Mauthner, M., Sharpe, S. *Family matters: communicating health messages in the family*. 1996. Family Health Research Reports, HEA, London.

3. Saunders, D. *Smoking cessation interventions: is patient education effective? A review of the literature*. 1992. London School of Hygiene and Tropical Medicine, London.

4. Gill, E., Sutton, S. 'Immunisation uptake: the role of parental attitudes.', in Hey, V. (ed.) *Immunisation research: A summary volume* 1998. HEA, London.

5. Rogers, A., Pilgrim, D. 'Non-compliance with childhood immunisation: personal accounts of parents and primary health care professionals', Unpublished.

6. Alderson, P., Barker, S., Henderson, J., Mayall, B., Pratten, B. 'Childhood immunisation: support to health professionals', in Hey, V. (ed.) *Immunisation research: A summary volume* 1998. HEA, London.

7. Bedford, H., Kendall, S. *Immunisation: health professionals' information needs – a review of the literature*. 1998. HEA, London.

8. Communicable Disease Surveillance Centre. 'Improvements in the control of whooping cough'. *Communicable Disease Report*, 1995; 5(30).

9. Department of Health. *Immunisation against infectious disease*. 1992. HMSO, London.

10. Salisbury, D.M. 'The future for childhood immunisation', *Current Paediatrics*, 1993; 3: 197–201.

11. Reflexions/Health Education Authority. *Childhood immunisation: the perspective of health professionals*. 1996. HEA, London.

12. Egan, S., Logan, S., Bedford, H. *Factors associated with low uptake of immunisation: the role for health education initiatives*. 1992. Unpublished report prepared for the HEA.

13. Bedford, H., Elliman, D. *Childhood immunisation: a review*. 1998. HEA, London.

14. Health Education Authority. *Health promotion and the family*. 1996. HEA, London.

1. Immunisation uptake: the role of parental attitudes

Elizabeth Gill and Steve Sutton
Health Behaviour Unit
Department of Epidemiology and Public Health
University College London

INTRODUCTION

A range of literature exists which implicates a number of factors in the low uptake of immunisation. These factors include:

- deficits in service provision;[1]

- social deprivation;[2]

- attitudes of health professionals;[3]

- parental attitudes;[4]

- inaccurate records.[5]

The literature is discussed further in two reviews;[6,7] suffice to note here that several studies have also used information held in child health computer systems to investigate the relationship between immunisation status and variables such as family size and maternal age.[8-11]

Apart from the Peckham Report,[4] which computed a simple attitude score and related it to immunisation status, only one study has compared groups of immunisation completers and non-completers on a range of attitudes and beliefs. Bennett and Smith (1992) studied three groups of parents in mid-Glamorgan: those who had fully vaccinated a target child against pertussis (n=85), those whose child partially completed the course (n=70), and those who refused to let their child receive the pertussis vaccination (n=73).[12] It was found that the group who refused differed significantly from the other groups in several respects: they reported more concern about long-term health problems as a result of pertussis vaccination, a lower risk of getting pertussis if not immunised, and attached a lower importance to pertussis vaccination. They also rated their child as more likely to get pertussis if immunised than those in the fully vaccinated group.

The HEA considered it crucial for its present strategy to obtain more detailed up-to-date information in order to develop health education materials and campaigns in this area. A review commissioned by the HEA identified a number of studies of parental attitudes but concluded that still further research was required.[13] The first research study described below was one of several commissioned by the HEA to meet this perceived gap in information.

THE ROLE OF PARENTAL ATTITUDES IN IMMUNISATION UPTAKE

The study design was simple – to survey a sample of parents whose children had been fully immunised and a sample of parents whose children had not been fully immunised. It aimed to provide information on parents' attitudes and beliefs and to enable comparisons between immunisation completers and non-completers. Furthermore, differences between these two groups would suggest factors that underlie parents' decisions and future health education could then target specific attitudes and beliefs held by non-completers, on the assumption that such differences in behaviour and belief would be amenable to alteration through information-based educational interventions. The study focused on early childhood immunisations, that is polio, triple vaccine (diphtheria, tetanus, pertussis – DTP), Hib (Haemophilus influenzae type b) and MMR (measles, mumps, rubella).

Study location

The study was conducted in two contrasting health districts in South East Thames Region, that is West Lambeth and Bromley, chosen to represent two contrasting settings – a deprived inner city district with a comparatively low uptake of immunisation and a more affluent suburban/rural district with a high uptake. Statistics from the COVER programme (Coverage of Vaccination Evaluated Rapidly) showed that, in August 1992 (the then latest available figures), coverage of third pertussis (P3) at 12 months was 77% in West Lambeth and 91% in Bromley.[14] The two districts also differed consistently in the coverage of other vaccines.

Figures from the latest census reveal that the two districts differ on virtually every demographic measure. West Lambeth is consistently 'worse' than Bromley in terms of population density, employment, housing, limiting long-term illness, and so on.[15] The findings from the study cannot be generalised to the rest of the country. To do this would have involved an altogether more ambitious and more costly study using systematic samples of health districts across the country.

Methods

The study data were derived from a cross-sectional survey of immunisation completers and non-completers. However, as the two groups were not subjected to a controlled comparison, the study offers *indicative* rather than *definitive* findings. Recruits to the study were found via the child heath surveillance system and random samples of immunisation completers and non-completers were drawn. *Immunisation completers* were defined as (the parents of) children whom the computer recorded as completing the course of three pertussis (whooping cough) immunisations. *Immunisation non-completers* were defined as (the parents of) children who had not completed the pertussis course. It is important to point out that this did not differentiate between refusers and those for whom the immunisation was contraindicated on medical grounds. Pertussis take up was treated as a convenient marker since pertussis non-completers included most of the polio, diphtheria and tetanus non-completers.

Data were collected by a face-to-face home-based interview with the carer (overwhelmingly the mother – 94% of respondents) of the target child using a lengthy structured interview schedule. Most questions were pre-coded but the questionnaire also contained some open-ended elements in order to collect more nuanced responses. The team undertook 759 full interviews, comprising 307 with completers and 452 with non-completers. The last category was deliberately over sampled since it was the behaviour, beliefs and attitudes of this group that were of most interest to the research sponsors. Technically, it was also important to allow for attrition within the non-completers group. Loss of cases was expected from the cumulative effects of the passage of time or as an unintended consequence of participating in the research.[16]

The study had a response rate of 57% in West Lambeth and predictably higher in Bromley at 68%. The attempt to increase response rates included the use of repeat visits and tracing movers. However, the West Lambeth location had a high mobility rate, common in the inner city. In addition, 20 addresses were thought too unsafe for interviewers.

Methodological issues

This section highlights the assumptions built into the research design and briefly discusses their consequent impact upon the data and their interpretation. It covers questions about the limitations imposed by working with official record sets and more fundamental points concerning the particular research model. Aspects of the social processes of research are also explored since these are important data in their own right.

Sampling

Both districts share the same child health system which is run by the South East Thames Regional Computing Bureau (RCB). However, immunisation services in the two districts are organised in different ways. The RCB generates the invitations for Bromley (although a small number of GPs opt not to use this system), while in West Lambeth, invitations are organised locally.

The sample was generated from the immunisation data base of the South East Thames RCB. This was a practical response to the need for cost-effective and systematic information. A sample devised from locality general practices was ruled out as too labour intensive and unreliable, and data from multiple sources can lack comparability. However, no sampling method is methodologically pure and it is important to recognise and allow for the limitations of working with official data. Some children always remain invisible to the surveillance systems and thus data may be inaccurate and outdated. There is therefore no absolute guarantee that a random sample of children drawn from the immunisation database will be representative of all children living in the geographical area covered by the database.

The sample was restricted to parents/carers of target children between 8 and 25 months. The lower limit was set to allow for the completion of primary immunisations (polio and triple vaccine) and for that information to be recorded on the database.

Defining completion

Analysis of the information from the sample yielded interesting distinctions between mothers' accounts of their child's immunisation status and the target child's respective computer records. Predictably, there was far greater convergence in the category of positive immunisation status. The computer-designated status of pertussis completer was confirmed by 91% of the group. In contrast, the sample assigned through computer records into the non-completers group produced only a 48% agreement to questions about non-completion. On further investigation, the researchers discovered that the target children concerned had only received one or two of the pertussis immunisations and yet self-reported as having all the requisite immunisations.

Parental self-representation

While it is important to verify all the causes of this discrepancy, it is an important finding in its own right. Other research into the complex of health behaviours, attitudes and motives offers one possible explanation: researchers have noted how the effects of compliance with 'the social desirability bias' influences health-related investigations.[17] Investigators have commented that this mostly affects the mother in her role as the manager of her family's health.[8] There is a strong possibility that mothers simply find it difficult to admit that they have not complied with the full demands of the immunisation programme.

A range of other influences may have prompted this movement (if it were real) – the serendipitous effects of participating in the study[16] or, more simply recall errors about the child's immunisation history. Relying on retrospective information is intrinsically prone to error. Quantifying these powerful effects is technically impossible but we need to bear it in mind in interpreting the data from the following study.

Theoretical paradigm

The study was centred on understanding distinctions and similarities between completers and non-completers. This analytic focus opened for scrutiny the respective motivation of two respondent groups or, more accurately, the representation of motives held among the respondents. The focus of data gathering was upon individual respondent's behaviours, attitudes and motives;

socio-economic group and other aspects of social location such as ethnicity and parental status were noted only if they were of statistical significance. The study specifically dismissed the notion that interventions should automatically assume a 'sociological' orientation by aiming at 'black mothers or single parent families'. On the contrary, it recommended interventions geared towards specific low take up sites and localities.

The survey questionnaire

The main areas covered in the questionnaire are presented below.

Section A. Most recent immunisation: venue; the health professional who gave the immunisation; the person who accompanied the child; satisfaction/ dissatisfaction with the last visit.

Section B. Immunisation history of the target child: reasons for non-immunisation; intentions to immunise child against Hib and MMR.

Section C. Other children: family size; any children with health problems; immunisation history of older siblings.

Section D. Immunisation intentions for future child: including reasons for not wanting particular immunisations.

Section E. Attitudes and beliefs: ratings of importance, safety and effectiveness of immunisations; perceived severity and incidence of diseases; use of and faith in homeopathic medicines.

Section F. Partner, health visitor, GP: perceptions of partner's, health visitor's and GP's attitudes towards immunisation; information and advice from these sources; partner's immunisation intentions for future child; likely and preferred venue for next immunisation.

Section G. Advertising and publicity: information about any advertising, information or publicity respondent had seen in the last 12 months.

Section H. Demographic details: including age of respondent; socio-economic group; ethnicity; housing tenure.

Demographic characteristics of the sample

Respondent's relationship to the target child

In 94% of cases the respondent was the natural mother of the target child; in 4% of cases the respondent was the natural father. The other 2% of respondents were foster mothers or other guardians/carers.

Gender of target child

Of target children 52% were male and 48% were female. No significant relationship was found between immunisation status and gender.

Age of target child

The target children's age at the time of the interview ranged between 9 and 27 months, with a mean of 16.8 months. Age of target child was not related to immunisation status. This was to be expected since both completers and non-completers were selected from the same specified narrow age range.

Age of respondent

The respondent's age ranged from 15 to 54 years, with a mean of 30 years. Over half the respondents were aged between 21 and 30. This factor was unrelated to immunisation status, that is there was no evidence that older (or younger) mothers were more (or less) likely to have had their child completely immunised.

Socio-economic group

Clearly, there are problems associated with accurately classifying the socio-economic group of women solely based on the occupation of the head of household.[19] The later discussion of housing tenure demonstrates a need for caution in premising findings on a one dimensional measure of socio-economic group. However, this measure does provide a usable, if somewhat crude, indicator of socio-economic group. The socio-economic group distribution as assessed by this single proxy indicator is shown in Table 1.1 below. Thirty-seven per cent of respondents came from the two lowest groups.

Table 1.1 Socio-economic groupings of respondents.

		% of total respondents
A	Upper-middle class	2
B	Middle class	20
C1	Lower middle class	22
C2	Skilled working class	18
D	Working class	9
E	Lowest level of subsistence	28

There was a tendency for more non-completers than completers to come from the lower groups, but this was not statistically significant.

Housing tenure

It is common to strengthen socio-economic group data by combining other indicators. This provides a composite determinant of socio-economic group location – housing tenure is one such key element of this index. Overall, 43% of respondents were owner-occupiers. Importantly, when housing tenure was considered (as distinct from occupational criteria) there was a significant association with immunisation status. More completers than non-completers were owner-occupiers (49% compared to 40% respectively), and correspondingly more non-completers lived in rented local authority housing (35% compared to 26% respectively). There is, therefore, an association between housing tenure and immunisation uptake.

Education

Two per cent of respondents were still in full-time education. Of the 98% who had left school or full-time education, 14% had left when they were less than 16 years old, 37% when they were 16, and 27% when they were 17 or 18. The mean age of leaving school or full-time education was significantly lower in non-completers than completers (17.3 years compared to 17.9 years respectively). Non-completers, then, had less formal education, but the difference was small (about six months on average).

Type of employment

The proportion of total respondents in the four main categories of employment are shown in Table 1.2.

Table 1.2 Employment categories of respondents

Employment category	% of total respondents
Works full-time	13
Works part-time	16
Unemployed	3
Looks after home or family	70

Note: Percentages sum to more than 100 because of multiple responses.

From the table we can see that 70% of respondents describe their main activity as looking after the home or family. This is not surprising given that 94% of the respondents were mothers of young children. Home-based interview surveys also tend to over-represent those people who spend most time at home. Importantly, the only significant relationship between immunisation status and type of work of respondents was that more completers than non-completers worked part-time (20% compared to 13% respectively). This phenomenon is worthy of further study.

Length of time respondent had lived at present address

The sample showed a fair degree of geographical mobility as 42% of respondents had lived at the current address for less than two years. A significant relationship was found between immunisation status and the length of time respondents had lived at their present address. A higher proportion of completers had lived at their present address for less than two years (see Table 1.3). As yet there is no plausible interpretation of this finding.

Table 1.3 Geographical mobility of respondents

Length of time respondent had lived at present address	% of non-completers	% of completers
<2 years	38	50
2–5 years	29	21
>5 years	34	29

Ethnic group

Self-reported ethnicity was assessed using a version of the 1991 census question. Only one person refused to answer. The majority of respondents (74%) were white, 18% were black (Black-Caribbean, Black-African, or Black-other), 4% described themselves as Asian (Indian, Pakistani, Bangladeshi), and the remainder were designated as 'other'. There was a tendency for the completers group to contain a higher proportion of whites and a lower proportion of black people.

Country of respondent's birth

Overall, 79% of respondents were born in the UK. There was no significant association between immunisation status of the child and whether or not the respondent was born in the UK. Of the 21% of respondents who were born outside the UK, 77% had been living in the UK for more than five years. There was no significant difference between completers and non-completers on this factor.

Country of target child's birth

Of target children 96% were born in the UK, compared to 79% of their parents. Only 6% of these children had been overseas for more than one month at a time. There was no significant difference between completers and non-completers on either of these factors.

SUMMARY

The sample consisted predominantly of mothers of young children. The socio-economic group distribution was 22% AB, 40% C1C2 and 37% DE; 43% were owner-occupiers. The sample comprised 74% of white people and 18% black. Only a minority were in paid work; most were looking after the home or family.

Crucially there were few important differences between completers and non-completers with respect to demographic characteristics. More completers were owner-occupiers, more worked part-time, more had lived at their present address for less than two years, and they had left school at a slightly older age on average than non-completers. On the other hand, there were no significant differences in socio-economic group (as defined through occupation of the head of the household) or ethnicity.

There was no evidence that time spent out of the country contributed in an important way to non-completion of immunisation.

The study has identified some of the important attitudinal factors in parental decision making. It also emerged from the data that families' material circumstances played a role in immunisation uptake. Specifically, access to a car or van was positively related to uptake. The study report did not attempt to engage with wider questions concerning the nature of the relations between material circumstances and individual behaviour, but it did note the statistical significance of such relations, if and when they occurred. The main research aim was to distinguish attitude differences between the completers and non-completers. However, it is possible that since the study did not uncover a large oppositional grouping of 'rational non-compliers' or immunisation dissenters,[20] we need to set additional explanatory accounts alongside attitudinal research.[21]

Nonetheless, this research study provides valuable insights into the distinctions between two groups of parents about their declared beliefs and attitudes. It also revealed some possible (and alterable) causes for non-compliance. These included for example, parents' uneven experience of the immunisation services. This finding could play a central part in contributing to the better delivery of the HEA's strategic aims. A discussion of the main survey findings follows.

DISCUSSION OF THE MAIN FINDINGS

Overall, the authors argue that health educators and professionals need to pay far more attention to acknowledging the complex and genuine threat parents experience in relation to the *immunisation decision* rather than to the communicable *diseases* such immunisations are designed to prevent. This was the most important finding across all the demographic groups surveyed who indicated worries about calculating risk in relation to their own child.

In terms of whooping cough vaccination, non-completion was strongly associated with two main groups of factors:

- most significantly, in-family understandings about the target child's pre-existing health problems (such as convulsions, asthma, allergies or fits) and fears that immunisation may trigger any of these;
- by negative parental experiences of health encounters with professionals.

The first set of factors was powerfully influenced by respondents' awareness of family members' health histories and appears to operate as a source of local family definitions of 'contraindication'.

Fear of whooping cough vaccine is still prevalent

Most importantly it is the *fear of immunisation* rather than the *disease* which is the source of maternal worry. Thus, the threat is seen to stem from the proposed intervention rather than the disease. This core finding is confirmed in other studies[21] and has important implications for how the HEA and childhood immunisation professionals proceed. Equally important in this respect is the related finding that the vast majority of non-completers do not present themselves as having anti-immunisation attitudes.

The three vaccines that cause most concern to parents are whooping cough, Hib and MMR. Whooping cough remains the *bête noire* of vaccines. Only 24% of respondents thought that whooping cough immunisation was completely safe and 6% thought it was very risky. Furthermore, of those respondents who said that there were immunisations they would not allow a future child to have, more than two-thirds mentioned whooping cough. Whooping cough was seen as particularly risky for a child who suffers from, or is predisposed to, health problems such as epilepsy, convulsions, fits, asthma, eczema and allergies. Parents expressed concern that the vaccine might interact with or trigger off such problems. This health concern was cited as the single *most prevalent reason* why parents had not had their child immunised against pertussis. Many parents were also concerned about other adverse effects, particularly brain damage, or had other less specific fears of the vaccine based on newspaper stories about negative reactions. Yet the study established that neither the presence in the family of a child with a health problem nor the number of children with a health problem was related to immunisation uptake. Furthermore, whether or not the target child was actually having regular treatment for a health problem was not connected to their immunisation status.

Such discrepancies indicate the methodological caveats of assuming a neat fit between attitude, behaviour and practices since the above finding clearly points to the difficulty of mapping one onto the other in health research.

Hib – 'untried and untested'

There is wide awareness of the Hib immunisation. However, Hib was specified by about 1 in 4 respondents who cited immunisations they would not want a future child to have. Immunisations are evidently subject to differential levels of consumer confidence. Parents were concerned that the Hib vaccine at the time was untried and untested. They did not feel that enough is known about its possible long-term effects. This raises the wider question about the processes involved in immunisation acceptability. Longevity coupled with lack of bad publicity about damaging reactions presumably play some part. Consumer resistance to new vaccines has also to be seen as part of a more widespread questioning of expert knowledge.[22]

MMR and other vaccines

Few respondents appeared to be worried about MMR in the same way as Hib in spite of the relative recency of its introduction. Nevertheless, parents were again concerned about possible harmful effects. Measles immunisation was also seen as the least effective as only 20% thought that it offered complete protection. Measles itself was regarded as fairly common but not serious: only 22% regarded it as very serious in 1995. Other vaccines give rise to far less concern. Only two respondents mentioned diphtheria as an immunisation they would not want a future child to have, and no-one mentioned polio, tetanus, or triple vaccine.

Parents feel uninformed

Given the complexity of immunisation schedules and the confusion caused by terms such as triple vaccines (for example, does this refer to three times or three types i.e. diphtheria, tetanus and pertussis?), many parents felt that they were not properly informed about childhood diseases and immunisations. In fact, 42% said that they would have liked more information about immunisation, particularly about the side effects and long-term risks of immunisation. They wanted clear information that would help them gauge whether their own child's reaction to an injection is normal or abnormal. They also wanted more information about what each immunisation does and how it works, how much protection the different immunisations provide, and the risks of not having their child immunised. One simple way of providing this information could be in the form of a 'fact sheet' for each separate disease/immunisation which could be given to the parents when the child was due to start a course of immunisation rather than at the immunisation visit itself.

Television was seen as the most popular and therefore the most important source of information about immunisation, followed by posters and leaflets in medical settings. Radio seems to be an under-used public information resource. Evaluating the effectiveness of advertisements on local radio would be worth considering. This particular medium may prove to be a cost-effective way of reaching home-based populations.

Health professionals could do more

A substantial minority of parents said they had received no information about immunisation from their health visitor. Crucially, a quarter of respondents were not even able to specify their health visitor's attitude towards immunisation. This finding could suggest that, in striving to be balanced, health visitors are experienced as having no preference.[21] The delicate task for health professionals is to strike a position that assuages disproportionate fears (especially in relation to the pertussis vaccine) without at the same time promoting the idea that immunisation decisions are above the calculation of risk.

In seeking information, respondents cited a range of possible professional sources, beyond health visitors. Surprisingly, few mothers could recollect the GP being a valuable information source. Only 17% could remember receiving any written information from their GP, whilst 37% had received verbal advice. This represents substantial lost opportunity for providing parents with accurate information.

If they wanted advice, most parents turned to one or other of the above sources, although some felt that GPs had a vested financial interest and were therefore not impartial.[21,23] Some respondents supported this view with reference to the incentive payments general practices receive in relation to coverage rates. Only a few would seek advice from a nurse, which is revealing given the high percentage of respondents who said that the most recent immunisation had been given by a nurse. If parents fail to see practice nurses as authoritative sources of information, the scope of their health educational role is restricted.

Complementary research on the attitudes and practices of key health professionals (that is GPs, health visitors, clinical medical officers [CMOs] and nurses) reveals a more complete picture of potential barriers to immunisation uptake described in this volume. Certainly, other studies indicate that perceived as well as actual divisions and differences inhibit the development of effective inter-professional working.

When offered a completely free choice of venue for the next immunisation, respondents cited a range of preferences, thus indicating the need for flexibility in the immunisation service. A quarter of all respondents would prefer to have their child immunised at home by a health visitor. This happens in only a very few cases. Other data[24] show that practical deterrents related to family size interfere with parents proceeding to immunisation completion – a finding that replicated the Peckham Report.[4] A more client-friendly service is demonstrably preferable to services designed more for the convenience of professionals.

Beliefs and attitudes

As already stressed, the most important differences between completers and non-completers were identified in terms of respondents' attitudes and beliefs about immunisation. Non-completers attached less importance to immunisations than completers and were less convinced that immunisations are safe and effective. In contrast, completers and non-completers did not differ with respect to their ratings of the severity and incidence of the different childhood diseases. In short, the two groups differed in their *beliefs about immunisations* but not in their *beliefs about diseases*. The direct implication of this finding is that health education campaigns and materials should focus particularly on providing information about the risks of immunisation compliance set against the risks incurred through contracting different childhood illnesses.

Immunisation 'runs in families': a child is more likely to be immunised if an older sibling has been immunised. One implication is that parents should be specifically targeted when they have their *first* child. It seems that whatever they decide to do with respect to the first child sets the pattern for later children.

Similarities between completers and non-completers

The apparent lack of demographic differences between completers and non-completers suggests that there may be little point in targeting black families, single parent families, families in which there are children with health problems, or younger rather than older mothers. Targeting is probably best done on a geographical basis (e.g. the GP practice or health district), concentrating on areas that are known to have a low uptake. However, further research is needed on the relationship between ethnicity and uptake.

The absence of differences between completers and non-completers with respect to whether their child minds having injections and whether the child has been overseas for more than one month at a time would seem to rule these out as important factors contributing to low uptake.

Although completers and non-completers did not differ in satisfaction with the last immunisation visit, satisfaction was related to *future* immunisation intentions. Those who were dissatisfied with the last visit were twice as likely to say there were immunisations that they would not allow a future child to have. Clearly it is important to try to reduce the incidence of bad immunisation experiences. Much of this has to do with the *quality of the interaction between patient and health professional*. Issues such as how the parent is treated by staff at all levels in the encounter, from receptionist to doctor, are very important in setting the tone. Parents make clear distinctions between encounters experienced as negotiation or coercion. Parents also expressed views about their needs for clear information and for time and space to digest and question any points of uncertainty. Equally valued were prior, not pre-emptory, discussions of possible immunisation reactions and advice about their management.

Where are the immunisation dissenters?

There were only a handful of parents in the sample defined as immunisation dissenters or rational non-compliers.[20] For example, only three out of over 100 respondents who gave a reason for not having their child immunised against whooping cough said that they did not believe in immunisation. This contradiction may well be an artefact of the research (namely the difference in power between interviewer and respondent which is to be expected given the state's interest in immunisation compliance). It may simply be easier to defend lack of completion of immunisation by personal narratives about health worries rather than to profess ideological antagonism to mass childhood immunisation.

Furthermore, 92% of immunisation non-completers thought it was important for their children to have all the recommended immunisations. Bearing in mind the extent to which 'rational non-compliers' come from the better educated and more powerful sectors of society and thus find it relatively easy to access the media, they could inflate the nature of immunisation worries as do the popular press. Nevertheless, it is important not to discount either the oppositionalists nor the 'scare stories' since both clearly indicate the existence of more diffuse forms of public disquiet about immunisation interventions.

Homeopathic medicine – more research needed

Most respondents had heard of homeopathy and about 1 in 4 had used herbal or homeopathic medicines to treat their children or to protect them against illness. Generally, however, respondents affirmed a belief in conventional immunisation. Nevertheless, immunisation non-completers had more faith in herbal medicine. Beliefs in homeopathy and herbalism may come to play an increasingly important role in influencing individuals' decisions about immunisation in the future. There is currently little research into alternative medicine as another form of expert knowledge. Detailed explorations of the use of alternative medicines in parental health management beliefs and practices would be valuable, particularly given that the grounds for homeopathy (especially the 'law of similars', that is small doses to protect against similar illnesses) appear superficially consistent with the rationale underpinning conventional immunisation.

References

1. Nicoll, A., Elliman, D., Begg, N.T. 'Immunization: causes of failure and tactics for success', *British Medical Journal*, 1989; 299: 808–12.

2. Jarman, B., Bosanquet, N., Rice, P., Dollimore, N., Leese, B. 'Uptake of immunisation in district health authorities in England', *British Medical Journal*, 1988; 296: 1775–8.

3. Pugh, E.J., Hawker, R. 'Measles immunisation: professional knowledge and intention to vaccinate', *Community Medicine*, 1986; 8: 340–7.

4. Peckham, C., Bedford, H., Senturia, Y., Ades, A. *The Peckham Report. National immunisation study: factors influencing immunisation uptake in childhood.* 1989. Action Research for the Crippled Child, Horsham.

5. Jefferies, S., McShane, S., Oerton, J., Victor, C.R., Beardow, R. 'Low immunization uptake rates in an inner-city health district: fact or fiction?', *Journal of Public Health Medicine*, 1991; 13: 312–7.

6. Bedford, H., Elliman, D. *Childhood immunisation: a review.* 1998. HEA, London.

7. Bedford, H., Kendall, S. *Immunisation: health professionals' views- a review of the literature.* 1998. HEA, London.

8. Li, J., Taylor, B. 'Childhood immunisation and family size', *Health Trends*, 1993; 25: 16–19.

9. Li, J., Taylor, B. 'Factors affecting uptake of measles, mumps, and rubella immunisation', *British Medical Journal*, 1993; 307,:168–71.

10. Pearson, M., Makowiecka, K., Gregg, J., Woollard, J., Rogers, M., West, C. 'Primary immunisations in Liverpool. I: who withholds consent?', *Archives of Disease in Childhood*, 1993; 69: 110–4.

11. Pearson, M., Makowiecka, K., Gregg, J., Woollard, J., Rogers, M., West, C. 'Primary immunisations in Liverpool. II: is there a gap between consent and completion?', *Archives of Disease in Childhood*, 1993; 69: 115–9.

12. Bennett, P., Smith, C. 'Parents' attitudinal and social influences on childhood vaccination', *Health Education Research*, 1992; 7: 341–8.

13. Egan, S., Logan, S., Bedford, H. 'Factors associated with the low uptake of immunisation: the role for health education initiatives'. 1992. An unpublished review commissioned by the Family and Child Health Division of the Health Education Authority, London.

14. Public Health Laboratory Service Communicable Disease Surveillance Centre. 'COVER' (Cover of vaccination evaluated rapidly). 1992; 23.

15. OPCS. *General household survey 1991*. 1993. HMSO, London.

16. Brannen, J., Dodd, K., Oakley, A. Getting involved: the effects of research on participants. Paper presented at BSA Conference Health and Society 25–28 March 1991, at University of Manchester.

17. Cornwell, J. *Hard earned lives: accounts of health and illness from East London*. 1984. Tavistock, London.

18. Holland, J., Mauthner, M., Sharpe, S. *Family matters: communicating health messages in the family*. 1996. HEA Family Health Research Reports, London.

19. Crompton, R., Mann, M. *Gender and stratification*. 1986. Polity Press, Cambridge.

20. Rogers, A., Pilgrim, D. 'Non-compliance with childhood immunisation: personal accounts of parents and primary health care professionals', Unpublished.

21. Alderson, P., Barker, S., Henderson, J., Mayall, B., Pratten, B. Childhood immunisation: support to health professionals'. 1997. In Hey, V. (ed.) *Immunisation research: a summary volume*. 1998. HEA, London.

22. Rogers, A., Pilgrim, D. 'The risk of resistance: perspectives on the mass childhood immunisation programme', in Gabe, J. (ed.) *Medicine, health and risk, sociology of health and illness monograph*. 1995. Blackwell, Oxford.

23. Reflexions/Health Education Authority. 'Childhood immunisation: the perspective of health professionals – a qualitative research report', in Hey, V. (ed.) *Immunisation research: a summary volume*. 1998. HEA, London.

24. Gill, E., Sutton, S. 'Immunisation uptake: the role of parental attitudes', in Hey, V. (ed.) *Immunisation research: a summary volume*. 1998. HEA, London.

2. *Childhood immunisation: support to health professionals*

Priscilla Alderson
Sandy Barker
Jacqui Henderson
Berry Mayall
Belinda Pratten

Social Science Research Unit
Institute of Education
University of London
18 Woburn Square, London

INTRODUCTION

Health visitor: *The more you think about it the more complex it gets.*

A significant minority of parents are concerned about the quality of service delivered during consultations about immunisation and cite dissatisfaction as a reason for their refusal to have their children immunised. The HEA has considered producing training materials for health professionals about childhood immunisation and so researched the views of health professionals about their immunisation work and their perceived need for information and training.

Consent and childhood immunisation

The Patient's Charter outlines the position and defines informed consent as the right to 'a clear explanation of any treatment proposed, including risks and any alternatives, before you decide whether you will agree to the treatment'.[1] Consent acts to protect patients from unwanted interventions, and professionals from litigation.

In relation to children's treatment consent has three elements:

- **understanding** – the law assumes that the ordinary person can understand enough to decide;
- **wisdom** – whereas adults can make any decision they choose for themselves, decisions for children have to be made in the child's best interests;

- **voluntariness** – the decision should be freely and willingly made, without any overt or covert coercion through fraud, force, threat or manipulative information.

Until children are competent to decide for themselves, parents have the legal responsibility to decide for them. The law is based on the assumption that parents can make informed and wise decisions, that they are the people most qualified to decide what is best for their own child, and that their sometimes onerous responsibility should be respected (for instance by professionals giving them the information and support they need).

However, the *Health of the Nation* programme,[2] implemented through government-funded targets, assumes that the potential benefits of childhood immunisation clearly outweigh the risks to children, individually and collectively. This can infer that parents who refuse are ignorant or foolish. It can also suggest that health professionals are better informed to take on the right to decide about the child's best interests.

SUPPORT TO HEALTH PROFESSIONALS

Aims of the study

- To investigate the needs of health professionals for support in their task of helping parents to make decisions about childhood immunisation.

- To make recommendations about appropriate training materials and opportunities for the delivery of primary healthcare workers' training.

Research methods

The study used a mixed method design carried out through semi-structured interviews with health professionals guided by a detailed topic list (see Appendix 1). The schedule also contained some closed questions that were coded and then analysed using the Statistical Package for Social Sciences (SPSS). As the interviews were planned to take about 45 minutes, the interviewers asked for an appointment of one hour. Interviewees were encouraged to offer examples of their experience and to expand on the topic in ways they felt appropriate. The interviewees were told that the project intended to provide information for immediate, practical use, that is to inform a decision by the HEA on training plans for professionals about immunisation.

Interviews were taped and responses were recorded on questionnaires, both in note form and by the use of selective transcription. The quantitative data were entered onto a computer-held database for analysis in terms of frequencies. The complete analysis covers both quantitative and qualitative parts. For brevity, the summary below only considers the qualitative aspect of the analysis. The quotations illustrate the range of opinions. In the original, the tables provide a quantitative framework to the quotations, showing clearly the percentage of interviewees holding each opinion.

Research questions underlying the interview sessions

- What do the interviewees perceive to be their role in immunisation?

- In the interviewee's view, how far does this perception accord with parents' understanding of professional roles and with the division of responsibility between parents and professionals?

- What does the interviewee identify as important issues cited by parents and, of these, which presents the most difficulties for the interviewee?

- How far do the interviewees consider that their role is on the one hand coherent and manageable and on the other hand conflicting? That is, are there conflicts between the public health and individual wishes and rights, and between government targets (and financial inducements) and parental and children's rights?

- How do interviewees rate their abilities as advisers and how successful do they consider their consultations to be?

- Do the interviewees consider that they are always able to offer honest and impartial advice about immunisation? What are the enabling and constraining factors?

- Do the interviewees consider that training materials, or other forms of support, would be useful to them and to (less experienced?) colleagues? What are their specific needs?

Respondents

Random sampling was impossible within the time constraints; practitioners were selected to obtain a reasonable balance of the four main professions. The 58 respondents constituted a 'convenience' sample and comprised GPs, CMOs, health visitors (HVs), practice nurses (PNs), a doctor working in management, a practice manager and a minority group's advocate (see Table 3.1). There were 43 women, and the 15 men were all doctors.

Table 3.1 The sample of interviewees

	Total	Inner city	Suburban	Rural
GPs	18	5	5	8
CMOs	9	5	2	2
HVs	16	4	8	4
PNs	2	3	5	4
Other	3	1	0	2
Total	58	18	20	20

Methodological points

The findings constitute exploratory data collected from 58 health professionals working in three different areas. The numbers are small and because they are not representative, generalising the findings is not possible. Nevertheless, the study draws attention to some indicative and important issues about practice especially the imprecision in defining and operating explicit guarantees about informed consent, intra-professional tensions, and the resultant inefficiencies in professional communication and practice.

PRESENTING THE QUALITATIVE FINDINGS

The analysis shows how people invoke experience to inform their stated views. Many quotations affirm the interdependent, almost symbiotic relations between themes. However, for clarity's sake the discussion is organised under some key issues which emerged:

- risk and benefit
- constraints on good practice
- pressure
- the professional role as 'government agent'
- ambiguity
- views about parents
- consent
- training and information materials – professionals' needs.

Risk and benefit

Professionals' views about parents' abilities to make informed, sensible decisions were mainly influenced by their beliefs about the benefit and harm of immunisation. If they believed immunisation to be almost entirely beneficial, then they saw less need to inform parents or to seek their consent, and they regarded refusal as negative and irresponsible. Alternatively, professionals who had reservations about immunisation were more concerned to warn parents about the nature and effects of the vaccinations, and were more likely to respect parents' own reservations.

Professionals expressed the view that parents tended to be most influenced by examples they saw or heard of concerning children who appeared to react adversely to immunisation.[3] In contrast, doctors tended to be equally influenced by their experiences, working in hospitals and abroad, of children suffering from the diseases:

> When I was a house officer the wards were full of children who hadn't been vaccinated and who had encephalitis. It was just horrendous to see the diseases that people don't see now. Parents have little idea of the significant effects of the diseases that we are protecting their child from. *(GP)*

Whereas GPs said they compared the possible effects of immunisation with the far more severe potential effects of the actual diseases, they thought mothers compared the possible effects with the baby's usual healthy state; that is, they were liable to use different measures for 'severe reaction'.

There were other more specific worries. Many professionals mentioned a dislike of 'putting needles into babies' and worried that it put their relationship with the family at risk. They were also concerned about physical effects:

> Remember what it was like to have your perfectly pure child contaminated with something? You're taking a risk and I'm sensitive to those feelings. (*GP*)

Some professionals reported no current concern about any of the vaccines, while others graded vaccines in a hierarchy of risk. While some discounted fears about pertussis, others reported continuing concern. These contradictory statements may say as much about the 'permission' health workers give parents to discuss concerns and the extent of their respect for parents' views as about the actual level of parental concern. They may also reflect professionals' own confidence. Some clearly had no doubts:

> I think parents' reports of any physical changes after immunisation are fairly accurate. The sensible ones don't report any problems much, only the not-sensible ones do. We used to find parents raising a lot of anxieties but that hardly happens now. (*GP*)

Constraints on good practice

Professionals were concerned about the following problems: 'giving parents more information than they can handle' and 'saturating them'; constraints of time; other people waiting in queues; lack of privacy in child health clinics; parents and professionals both having limited time for discussion; crying babies and older children disrupting discussions:

> My main feeling is frustration. The main reason I don't practise as I'd like is the time constraint. I feel, I could have done better but there is a waiting room full of people. More and more people are coming to see me for less and less of a problem. I see 50 to 80 a day. (*GP*)

Some interviewees struggled against this pressure: 'If I haven't got time, I make time'. There may be a gendered effect in the willingness with which professionals imparted information. GPs, mostly male, were generally against giving much information:

> I don't offer information if I'm not asked. If you go jabbering on about side effects that could possibly happen, the hazards and benefits, and all that lot, people get apprehensive. I go blindly on, I've never seen a serious reaction of any kind. Yes I keep adrenalin on the shelf, but I've never checked to see if it's out of date. I believe in immunisation, so the parents automatically do. (*GP*)

Some professionals stressed communication skills, listening and reassuring. However, the belief that a 'question-and-answer session' was the most effective format required professionals to take account of whether parents felt able and willing to ask a chain of questions; and to consider what measures they might take to enable parents to do so during a consultation. They tended to see their work as informing but not pressuring parents; they reported giving detailed information to parents. Sharing benefit with other children was an asset that professionals mentioned or wanted to explain. Some chose to see this rationale as a critique of class privilege:[3]

> The class thing irritates me. It's the working class protecting the chosen few [who refuse] and who have access to private medicine if they have any problems. *(HV)*

The theme of risk was omnipresent in the respondents' interviews and included issues such as the perceived risks of giving so many immunisations in so short a period, the different levels of worry for each vaccine, the importance of giving parents time to discuss risk and benefit with relevant interested people, immunisation as a process with decisions being made at each point along the line in the light of risk, the pros and cons of alienating parents who think risk outweighs benefit, the professional's juggling of reassurance, explanation and discussion, and the practical pressures of clinics in terms of time, queues and crying babies.

Pressure as a function of professional convictions

Professionals legitimised exercising pressure through convictions about the benefits of immunisation, and the folly of refusing it:

> I bring varying pressure to bear, depending on how important I think the vaccine was. I would try very hard with polio. *(CMO)*

Some interviewees gave contradictory replies, partly in that they changed their expressed views and partly in that they mixed statements of respect with criticisms of parental choice. Professionals spoke of discussion with mothers as if both adults had equal status and authority: 'We're sitting at a round table, that shows that we start at an equal level'. However, this view denies the power dynamics in consultations. As one interviewer noted: 'I felt steamrollered by this GP and wondered whether parents do'. This particular GP interpreted parents' reservations as emotional, in the dismissive sense, but she also had reservations about coercion:

> Back in the time when there was a surge of emotion about whooping cough vaccine I couldn't put my hand on my heart and say it was safe, so I left it to parents to decide and didn't push anyone. It was a very emotional time. Mothers on TV with brain-damaged children. Now I can be happy to do it. I try to talk to the homeopathic ones, but they are people with fixed ideas, you're up against a brick wall. It's almost a waste of time, but I try to explain the useless path they're going down. But it's a free country, and if the parent chooses not to do it, it's on their conscience, not mine. *(GP)*

GPs' views about their dilemmas as implementers of public health policies and as family doctors highlight many contradictions inherent in a liberal democracy. The abiding resistance of some groups of predominantly white middle class parents (who prefer a homeopathic approach) was an exemplary instance.

The professional as 'government agent'

Over half the interviewees identified with the idea of their being 'government agents', with a third accepting this position and 22% uneasy about it. A female CMO contrasted the political with the personal, but ended on an overtly political note:

> I find it's all very difficult that timing targets are set; babies are so different and some are very small. The targets make everyone more unhappy. Mothers are given less choice and are under more pressure. GPs accuse me of immunising their patients, as if they're only interested in the payments, but I can't turn them away when they turn up here. Health issues shouldn't be due to payment, it should be for the health of the nation. *(CMO)*

Some professionals thought that parents did not know about targets, or would not understand them. Others described how their non-medical friends had told them of being taken off GPs' lists. Additionally, frequent mention of health visitors being 'good at chasing people up' emphasised an inspection rather than a support role. Targets appeared to some professionals to set them in competition with each other and to exacerbate intra-professional rivalries:

> I think they should close the baby clinics. I should not have to be responsible for following up their sequelae. GPs should be responsible for doing immunisation. We know how the parents will react, we know the babies, we can keep proper records. *(GP)*

Communicating with non-English speaking mothers was a common concern in the inner and outer city areas.[4] One Asian practice nurse who spoke Hindi had been assigned to a GP practice by the Family Health Service Authority (FHSA). She criticised health visitors who told mothers about the child health clinic but not about immunisation at the surgery:

> The mothers have a great deal to discuss with me. Lots of them with a 5-year-old want that child to have the Hib. The families move around such a lot, moving house, going back to Asia for a while, we have to spend time with them sorting out records. When they have concerns I suggest they chat to the doctor. We must respect parents' rights. *(PN)*

In contrast, some doctors, who were among those who argued for the benefits rather than concentrating on the risks of immunisation, were happy with targets. A doctor working mainly in administration replied:

> Targets have brought the worst up to the standard of the best, and improved data collection. You have to accept that if you want something, you've got to pay for it. *(GP)*

Although it would be wrong to draw any generalisation from this work, some doctors thought that the *Patient's Charter*[1] encouraged undesirable tendencies; 'It leads to a moaning public and a selfish society. All relationships have been made one-sided'. In rural areas many professionals thought that no-one had heard of the Charter. In city areas some professionals considered that patients were already too demanding before the advent of the Charter.

Ambiguity

Interviewees reflecting on questions of risk revealed a high level of ambivalence. A consultant in communicable disease control described speaking to a group of health visitors and school nurses and saying:

> Stick your hand up if you think the introduction of the Hib vaccine is worthwhile, considering the expense and all the rest. I should think about half thought it was worthwhile and half not. They're the same – compliant but troubled.

Pressurising a mother to have a vaccine might lead to disaffection with the professional or with the preventive health services more generally.[3] A female CMO, who asked not to be taped but who agreed to notes being made, spoke of:

> ... seeing each baby as if he was my own. Maybe I worry even more than if he was my own sometimes. It's very important to get it right. I'm completely committed to the programme of immunisation. But I don't like immunising babies who are 'off-colour', not because of possible damage, but because parents will attribute illness to the vaccine and become anxious about the whole programme. Parents' anxiety is as important as the child's physical side effects. So I accept dissent, which is very infrequent, usually only to part and not the whole programme. Parents don't have 'official' reasons for not immunising, but often it is a good reason for them. *(CMO)*

Another GP explored a different type of dissent generated by fundamental differences of theoretical views:

> I would prefer to have a general information paper that I can present to them, which reviews the literature. But often we're talking from different perspectives of science, so it's not helpful. They bombard me with their theories and I may bombard them with mine, but we may not be on the same wavelength. But we generally achieve a consensus, and if they want one or some of the immunisations, then that's fine. I feel unable to give the authoritative answer. *(GP)*

Concern about responsibility for taking risk was another area of ambiguity. Professionals spoke of the difficulty of managing risk in an uncertain legal context. Some commented that the changed policy on immunisation schedules undermined confidence in the scientific rationale for immunisation.

Views about parents

Some professionals expressed sympathy about parental dilemmas, but many were dismissive:

> One of my kids was unwell for some weeks after being immunised so I can sympathise with parents. But one of my friends, who's a GP, didn't have his kids done, and one caught it and was quite ill. It changed his outlook. If you are having your own kids done, you have a natural level of anxiety which is big enough to make you worry about whether you should have them done or not. It's reasonable for parents to have that, but it's not a real anxiety. *(GP)*

Some health professionals described consent as a passive matter of reassuring mothers:

> Consent is to know what injections the child is going to have, to know what they protect against, and that their child is considered healthy enough to participate.

Several accounts illustrated professional unease about dissenting parents and about pressuring them. They looked for clues about how seriously to accept the parents as responsible, reasonable people. They are influenced by how cooperative and responsive the parents are to other professionals. This can lead to a double bind when parents who are seen as uncooperative are assumed to be irresponsible. Respondents contrasted parents' 'natural' and 'irrational' anxieties with doctors' scientific and expert knowledge. However, a few professionals held more complicated notions than implied in this simplistic dichotomy:

> The higher the social class, the higher the anxiety, and the more the medical profession is questioned. Which is right? To look into it more deeply but create worries? We have a good practice nurse who puts it across very well and they relate to her. *(GP)*

Variability in professional practices regarding consent

Professionals were asked what they understood by 'consent'. Some emphasised *implied consent*:

> Parents give consent for the child by bringing it. We go by intent rather than a consent form. *(HV)*

> Consent is about compliance. We need to do more work on how to get them to comply, to take it up. *(HV)*

The idea of implied consent, that parents who attend an immunisation session in effect consent to it, is reasonable if parents are aware of this and they are not attending solely for other reasons. The securing of informed consent should operate equally in opportunistic immunisation. The Code of Practice Pursuant to the Mental Health Act 1983, 1989,[5] offers a very stringent definition of informed consent. This lays down that consent is not a blanket agreement in advance, but should be sought at the time of each procedure. In some areas mothers are asked to sign a form to show that they are willing to attend the immunisation programme. This sign of respect can also raise problems, as mothers may feel that they 'signed away their rights'.

In other settings, with no formal safeguards, implied consent could easily merge into the paradox of *coerced* 'consent':

> I would hope my intellectual arguments would hold sway. Unfortunately a lot of parents are unable to take these on board, and you have to use a little bit more in terms of persuasion. I feel comfortable with that. My duty is to the child, and not to have the child immunised because of grandmother's prejudice is unacceptable as far as I'm concerned. Lawyers talk of informed consent. If parents bring the child in full knowledge of what is involved, and the balance of risks against profits, we don't get parents to sign. I sign over the stamp we have. The nurse asks if there's anything they want to ask. The fact that they've brought their child for immunisation is informed consent. When new parents join, we have all the immunisation forms given to us, and we won't register a child without them. If parents refuse that will sway us against having the child on the list. If a child comes in and I notice the child hasn't had them, I sometimes will do them opportunistically. I think targets have improved rates. There's no doubt that money talks, and it's meant a lot of GPs have got themselves sorted out. *(GP)*

This view assumes that parents understand the nature and purpose of the procedure, the risks, benefits and any alternatives, as the *Patient's Charter* describes.[1] With non-English speaking parents this may not be so. Another GP would prefer compulsory immunisation:

> ... because they've read some scare story in the *Sun*. It's these watchdog programmes that cause problems. That makes life very difficult for us because obviously you don't want conflict but you want to protect the child and the community. I wouldn't want to force the issue but on one or two occasions I have referred them to the paediatrician at the hospital, who always backs up my judgement. If they still refuse it boils down to emotion at the end of the day, it's not logic. Rather than compel the patient to have it, it would be nice if it was government policy that every child entering school would have a certificate saying that their vaccinations were up to date. That would take a lot of the heat off us, and would encourage parents to realise that it is their duty. But it would have to be backed up by a genuine policy of giving help to patients who have problems, compensation should be automatic. *(GP)*

One health visitor however, notes the dangers in undermining the current voluntary scheme:

> I have heard a GP actually threatening to remove the mother from his list. Whether it's just bluff, it's still being said, and I think it's unprofessional and totally unfair. *(HV)*

Some professionals respected consent as *formally making and signifying a decision*. But the practice of issuing consent forms was not universal. Not one professional interviewed gave outright agreement to the idea that they should decide in the case of immunisation, although some thought there could be a case for this:

> Well I suppose yes, in a few exceptional cases professionals should make the ultimate decision that a child should have immunisation, if it's in the child's best interests. *(CMO)*

Despite reservations about consent at the level of beliefs and the unevenness of consent procedures, most professionals thought that they should not have the right to decide:

> It would be outrageous if professionals could decide. I've never thought about that. You must have a let-out for people with religious objections. There is this let-out in the US and it is very liberally applied.

Training and information materials – professionals' needs

Some professionals said that they did not need training and did not have time for it. GPs remarked that immunisation came very low down on their list of concerns; it was routine, 'just something I have to do'. Some felt that paperwork was the main problem raised by immunisation. Others were more engaged in the issues it raised. Health visitors in particular wanted to know about opportunistic immunisation and legal cover for this. They were worried about giving immunisation in the child's home and about the risk of anaphylaxis. One health visitor found training on serum administration and storage very useful:

> We also talked about anaphylaxis and it's recommended to stay for a good 20 minutes afterwards, but often that's forgotten about. It is extremely rare, but that's not entirely satisfactory. *(HV)*

Nearly three-fifths of professionals thought they needed training, and the same number thought that their colleagues did. A common response was to say that members of other professional groups, but not their own, needed training:

> I definitely think the practice nurse who gives the vaccinations needs updating. She doesn't like giving them when a child is slightly unwell but it is not contraindicated. I would support her in that, she shouldn't have to do anything unless she's happy. She won't do opportunistic vaccinations because she doesn't think she's covered and that causes a lot of confusion. I think these conflicts are the most difficult part of immunisation. We're all supposed to be working together. But it doesn't seem right for GPs to put pressure on parents because they're going to be paid! *(HV)*

Health visitors tended to say that their training was very good on communication skills, but that other professions would benefit from more training on these:

> I hope the HEA will be looking at communication skills, they're so important. It is helping to change attitudes and helping people to say the things they really need to say, without feeling threatened or small or

belittled, and it's learning to pick up on body language. I need to know more about the rationale for homeopathic immunisation, what research has been done into its effects and how to respond to parents who believe in it. *(HV)*

Some interviewees spoke for themselves:

I sat in on one or two clinics but had no real training for this. I once did some training where we videoed our sessions with parents and then all discussed them afterwards. That was very useful. I'd like to be able to discuss differences of opinion as a group, and the sorts of issues we should be raising with parents. I'd like regular updates, and seminars on progress and developments. It's difficult getting hold of the existing material, let alone new stuff. We need a specific leaflet on pertussis for people who are concerned. *(CMO)*

Speaking of financial incentives, a health visitor said:

Money talks. Training is now for health visitors and practice nurses, but you won't get GPs going unless you pay them. *(HV)*

Like other professionals she thought that two types of leaflets would help – simpler general ones and a more detailed set to give to parents who expressed extra concerns. The advocacy service coordinator thought that training was needed on consulting with groups of parents about their understanding and their needs:

At some practices they have brainstorming sessions with all the staff having something to offer. Backup material needs to be provided locally in the community languages.

Interviewees offered differing views on leaflets for parents. 'Some people don't read leaflets. We need leaflets with a wider range of reading levels, and in other languages.' One health visitor thought the DoH 'green book'[6] was 'wonderful, I keep it in the car and keep checking up on it when I'm quizzed by extremely intelligent parents'. Some city staff lent their green book to parents. One CMO commented: 'We need stuff related to what's in the news, and we need it quickly'.[4] Many professionals thought that HEA leaflets were useful but that they were 'always running out, we need a much better supply'. As they were worried about running out, they were cautious about giving them out.

Some information needs were very specific:

I want pamphlets on each separate vaccine about contraindications for each one, and to actually document anaphylaxis treatment, what to do if a child reacts badly, doses of adrenalin and that sort of thing. It also raises the confidence of parents to see you working to a protocol. *(HV)*

One of the most helpful things is the Department circular on consent (1992). Parents already know most of the things in the leaflets before they read them. If they turn to a leaflet, they want more information, which properly presents both sides of the picture, so that they can make an informed choice. The HEA leaflet on measles really is dreadful, an emotive appeal to parents' fears, the crying child with the impression given that parents have no choice. I want to present it that parents *do* have a choice; they could delay for a few months. *(HV)*

The above comments record a range of professionals' views about training needs. The next section draws out some further policy implications of the data. There is a focus both on identifying some practical actions to increase professional understanding and improve practice in respect of managing immunisation in the context of parental concerns.

PRACTICAL AND POLICY IMPLICATIONS ARISING FROM THE STUDY

The immunisation of babies and small children raises unique problems in interactions between health professionals and their clients. There are no simple findings and no simple conclusions. This study can only suggest broad recommendations to guide the development of policy and practice. Nevertheless, the research points to some major training needs in relation to the role of health professionals in the delivery of immunisation. These possible topics for training are summarised below.

Immunisation is a contested practice

Conflicting values are *integral* to discussion of childhood immunisation. This raises the question, what sort of society do we want? Ideally one that is both free of infectious diseases and respectful of social dissent. A necessary tension inheres between these two desirable goals. Notably, people will disagree on the following:

- Is risk to a few acceptable in the interests of protecting the population?
- How important is informed consent, and how far should it be negotiated before it should be overridden?
- What should be the relative power and responsibility of the health care service staff and of parents?

Power relations are inherent in all health decision making

Expert, experienced and very knowledgeable professionals have to work hard if they are to avoid presenting their expertise as standards or rules to which parents must accede. How far can, or should, parents demand access to this knowledge in order for them to make an informed choice? What are the practical obstacles to genuine informed discussions? Considerable ethical problems also arise from differential access to private alternative expert knowledges such as homeopathy? Should parents be able to refuse immunisation if this means that their child is removed from a GP's list and may be unlikely to be accepted onto another? What are the health implications of this threat to non-conforming parents and their children?

Self-evidently the level of parental education and socio-economic position is a factor in immunisation decisions. The 'difficulty-makers' among parents were commonly the most well educated. These people claimed to have, and were sometimes recognised as having, good levels of knowledge about the issues. As a few people argued, the well children of well-educated parents are, through not being immunised, jeopardising the health of more vulnerable children, often of less well-educated parents.

The effect of the division of labour on how parents experience the immunisation intervention

At the general level of their terms of employment, and in relation to immunisation specifically, nurses' and doctors' work differs. As noted earlier, only mothers (usually) see through all stages of the immunisation process. Each professional group has partial knowledge of what babies and mothers go through and each has incomplete experience of dealing with a mother-baby duo. This division of labour at practical levels has important implications for training work (see below).

TACKLING THE ISSUES

1. In order to formulate a policy about training interventions it may be useful to group the types of professional responses, in order to increase the chances of understanding interactions between professionals and parents. People can be broadly (but not easily) divided into holding three kinds of views:

   (a) immunisation is an undisputed good, with certain minimal risks;

   (b) immunisation brings important benefits, but also involves risks and uncertainties;

   (c) the risks of immunisation, such as the timing, or particular vaccines, or for particular children, can be greater than the desired benefits.

This grouping is one way of thinking about the professionals in the sample. Although this study has no data on parents beyond what the professionals say, for the sake of argument, parents can be assigned to these categories too. It can then be said that:

- group (a) parents tend to want little discussion;

- careful discussion helps group (b) parents to accept immunisation for their children;

- group (c) parents will probably refuse.

- If a group (a) professional is dealing with a group (c) parent, they are unlikely to agree on a compromise. Other work has drawn attention to the same potentiality.[3] Training which is aimed to increase immunisation rates is often primarily concerned with group (b) and (c) parents. There is a need to think more deeply about the underlying value differences at play in debating the immunisation decision. This leads to the next point.

Communication skills – a problematic phrase

Caution is needed in using the phrase 'communication skills'. Communicating is affected by the knowledge-bases and the goals being discussed. If, therefore, the two interactants have different understandings of the value of immunisation as a national programme, improving skills may have little impact on the outcome. 'Communication skills' were frequently mentioned as a mere 'technique'. If the techniques are to aid communication, they need to be more than a veneer of behaviours. Rather, they need to be the expression of intrinsic respect and concern. Professionals who respect their clients are willing to believe that their own knowledge may, on a few occasions be provisional, and that the client has a different knowledge which can positively contribute to health decisions.

Several practitioners thought courses could help them to understand more about parents' beliefs and experiences. This understanding could be best achieved if parents holding a range of views shared in running the courses. This would clearly radically alter the tenets of much professional training. There is a paradox in that courses in communication help professionals to feel more expert and highly qualified, yet this can distance them from their clients. Alternatively, informal and relaxed contact with patients can aid mutual respect and understanding. Many professionals mentioned the value of not appearing to push parents into a decision, leaving time for them to change their view and accept immunisation. This approach could be valuable for group (b) parents who are troubled by conflicting information and who want to feel that their decision is made in the best possible way with due thought and care. The techniques can be used by group (b) and (c) professionals with group (c) parents to satisfy one another that the decision has been carefully discussed and, even if they differ, there is mutual respect between the adults on which to base the child's future shared health care. However, for group (a) professionals with group (c) parents, who adamantly disagree and reject one another's values, the skills can increase confusion and misunderstanding. They can give the appearance of respect. Frequently practitioners reported abandoning listening skills, since they noted either 'It's a waste of time talking to them', or 'If they don't come to be immunised I tell them not to come back'.

The strengths and limits of the communication skills approach in different contexts needs acknowledgement. Communication skills training is not a panacea for all disagreements; when there is a conflict of aims, communication skills can increase confusion by giving a misleadingly open-ended and democratic impression. Skills developed through 'non-directive counselling' in which the client's own views are the main issue,[7] are not unproblematic. Their application is limited when the professionals' sole aim is to redirect the views of resisting clients.

Interviewees generally preferred videos to lectures. They mainly thought that it was more worthwhile to exchange, challenge and refine one another's views, than to sit listening to talks which they could as easily read. Discussion, role play and looking at personal values, as well as skills, were thought to be important.

The HEA could increase the possibility of discussion with objecting parents by addressing their rational concerns.[3] This could encourage respect for parents' demanding and responsible position, rather than appealing to parents' fear and guilt. A range of leaflets is called for; for instance, some could respond to homeopathic arguments with summaries of research reviews and statistics. Ensuring a ready supply of leaflets could help to increase parents' information, and to encourage professionals routinely to share more detailed discussion with parents. The leaflets could include suggestions of questions which parents might wish to raise.

There are several ways of managing conflicts of power and interest.[8] A common way is to avoid considering the actual conflict, and to concentrate instead on technique: to discuss not *whether* to do things but *how* to do them, for instance through using communication skills. This tactic sidesteps the central unresolved dilemmas facing professionals who immunise babies. These, as the data make clear, include clinical, professional and personal uncertainty.

Many professionals read as a means to update their knowledge, and some attend discussion groups and find them useful. However, emphasis on training in communication skills can divert attention from improving the *substance* of discussions and making sure staff understand the available information. It is important for staff, especially within teams, to discuss basic clinical, legal and ethical aspects of their immunisation work. There are still issues of power outstanding. Professional divisions in primary health and those between professionals and their patients reflect (and constitute) the relations of socio-economic group, race and gender. Training materials and pedagogies need to be sensitive to these social divisions if they are to be fully effective.

Childhood immunisation adds further complications to dilemmas raised by treatment for sick adults. Each person has to find his or her own compromise and when values conflict there are no wholly satisfactory means of resolving them. This accounted for the way professionals in this study qualified earlier statements, contradicted themselves, and upheld a range of values within one interview. It also explains why it was hard to classify someone as authoritarian or libertarian, for many people combined both approaches.[3] Training courses, which recognise and then consider how to reconcile opposing values and how to practise in teams where team members have differing values and goals, could help health staff to clarify their own position. They could lead them to conclude that 95% immunisation rates, though from some points of view unsatisfactory, allow for appropriately flexible primary health care services in a pluralist society.

RECOMMENDATIONS

In the context of the study findings, the following broad recommendations are indicated.

Education on basic issues

The areas of concern are basic ones – consent, professional activity in a democracy, power and the division of labour. Many interviewees were struggling with these issues. In-service education on the clinical, legal and ethical aspects of immunisation work is recommended.

Training targeted at groups who work together

Training some staff, or some types of staff, was likely to be less useful than training groups together. Rather than sending nurses or GPs on a day's course, trainers/educators could come to the practice or clinic and work with the group. This is an expensive and time-consuming option, but it could serve to clarify people's values and to suggest practical ways of raising agreed standards.

Providing a range of literature

As some professionals have proposed, it would be useful to provide at least two levels of written information – simple ones and more detailed ones for those who would like them. These might, like other health education leaflets, suggest questions parents may wish to raise. Planning the simpler leaflets should involve more consideration of the minimal amount of information parents need if they are to make informed decisions about immunisation.

Commissioning two- and three-sided research studies

As Bedford and Kendall (1994) point out, there have been few studies of both parental and professional understandings of their own positions and of each other's[9] and, as far as we know, virtually no published studies of interactions regarding immunisation between the two 'sides'. Such studies would increase understanding of practices and means of improving them.

Children are absent from the discussion. A few mentions were made of children's own retrospective or hypothetical views. From both theoretical and practical standpoints, three-sided research studies are urgently needed to explore children's, parents' and health professionals' knowledge, views and behaviour.

References

1. Department of Health. *The Patient's Charter*. 1991. HMSO, London.

2. Department of Health. *The Health of the Nation: a consultative document for health in England*. 1991. Cm 1523. HMSO, London.

3. Rogers, A., Pilgrim, D. 'Non-compliance with childhood immunisation: personal accounts of parents and primary health care professionals', Unpublished.

4. Reflexions/Health Education Authority. 'Childhood immunisation: the perspective of health professionals', in Hey, V. (ed.) *Immunisation research: a summary volume*. 1998. HEA, London.

5. Department of Health. *Code of practice pursuant to section 118 (4) of the Mental Health Act, 1983*. 1990. HMSO, London.

6. Department of Health. *Immunisation against infectious disease*. 1992. HMSO, London.

7. Rogers, C. *On becoming a person*. 1961. Constable, London.

8. Gouldner, A. *The coming crisis in western sociology*. 1978. Heinemann, London.

9. Bedford, H., Kendall, S. *Immunisation: health professionals' information needs – a review of the literature*. 1998. HEA, London.

APPENDIX 1 TOPIC LIST

The questions were developed into the following topic list and used as an agenda for the interviews.

A. How long have you worked in this post and with parents on immunisation?

What do you think you have learned about this work during this period?

B. What are the specific issues that parents raise in this area?

Are there any specific problems they raise?

C. How do you deal with any reservations? What do you do if they dissent or default?

D. Please tell me about a memorable interaction with parents about immunisation.

Make sure you cover:
What happened?

What issues were raised, and by whom?

How easy/difficult was it?

What was the outcome?

How happy/satisfied was the professional with the meeting?

What is the professional's assessment of level of parents' satisfaction with the meeting?

E. What further examples can you describe in order to highlight issues, difficulties, conflicts in these interactions?

Try to get at least two examples, one difficult and one easy, in their terms.

F. How comfortable are you in this immunisation work?

Do you perceive any conflicts within work with parents on immunisation?

What are your own views on the safety and efficacy of immunisation?

What would/did you decide about your own children?

How would/do you feel about this now?

G. How far and in what ways do governmental policy interventions, such as targets, guidelines and advice, and financial arrangements, play a part in affecting professional behaviour?

What are the useful, enabling or constraining impacts of government interventions?

H. What are your views on consent?

Can parents be informed, and make the best decisions for their baby?

Should professionals take final responsibility for decisions about a baby's health care?

I. How far do you think your communication skills are adequate for the task of advising parents?

What are your particular merits?

Have you had any training? Have your colleagues?

What do you and/or your colleagues need to learn/do?

J. You may know that the HEA is planning to provide materials/resources for health professionals to help them to discuss immunisation with parents. Do you have any suggestions for support/training materials? For yourself? For less experienced colleagues? Can you suggest content, style/form?

3. Childhood immunisation: the perspective of health professionals

Reflexions Communication Research
7 King Street, London

INTRODUCTION

For a number of years, the HEA has run public education campaigns in order to promote the availability of childhood immunisations. As part of its ongoing planning and development, the HEA has commissioned seven waves of opinion polling to gauge mothers' perceptions about, and knowledge of, childhood disease and immunisation. The tracking has also measured levels of satisfaction about their most recent immunisation visit. Several important concerns have emerged. These are:

- increasing levels of dissatisfaction with immunisation services;
- decreasing levels of confidence about the safety and efficacy of some immunisations;
- insufficient choices about whether and when to have their child immunised.

HEALTH PROFESSIONALS' PERSPECTIVES OF CHILDHOOD IMMUNISATION

Research objectives

In order to inform future strategic planning and policy development the overall research objective of the study reported here was to establish ways in which the HEA can best support health professionals to improve the delivery of childhood immunisation services. Within this broad objective, the study aimed to:

- discover what health professionals understand as parents' needs, knowledge and concerns about immunisation;

- compare their understandings with their reaction to findings drawn from two sources (that is tracking studies and an evaluation of a recent radio campaign);

- determine the nature and extent of health professionals' training needs;

- identify which of these needs might be effectively addressed by the HEA and in what form.

The research method

A two-part qualitative study was conducted with health professionals involved in the immunisation programme. The first stage consisted of an exploratory pilot study comprising nine individual interviews to provide a more detailed understanding of the key issues:

- three with GPs;

- three with practice nurses;

- three with health visitors.

Within the pilot phase, the sample consisted of professional groupings drawn from a geographical spread (Barnsley, Leicester, and Gillingham), a mix of urban and rural locations, and a mix of practice arrangements (single GP, group or health centre; fundholding or non-fundholding). These findings were then used to guide the second and main stage.

The second phase comprised a set of 17 focus/discussion groups, arranged in two ways as shown in Table 5.1:

Table 5.1 Second phase interview groupings

3 interviews with each single professional grouping of:	2 interviews with each mixed professional grouping of:
GPs alone	GPs and practice nurses
Practice nurses alone	GPs and health visitors
Health visitors alone	Practice nurses and health visitors
	GPs, practice nurses and health visitors

The focus groups were conducted in nine different locations in England, including: northern industrial towns, midlands conurbations and southern commuter sites. Within these locations discussants were recruited again from a mix of urban and rural locations and a mix of practice arrangements. Care was also taken to include professionals from more affluent and less affluent settings, so as to encompass health professionals who had experience of, and understandings about, working with ethnically and socially diverse communities.

The focus/discussion group process

The interviews took place between 14 October and 4 November 1996 and the research findings were presented to the HEA on 18 November 1996.

At the beginning of each discussion, health professionals were asked to state what they currently saw as the key issues in relation to child immunisation. Each concern was explored in more detail, using the following questions.

- What were health professionals' own views with regard to the issue?

- What did they understand as the point of view of parents with regard to the issue?

- [as appropriate] What light could they shed on other evidence from the tracking studies and the evaluation of the radio campaign? (The statements which were presented from the tracking studies and the radio campaign evaluation are given in tinted boxes.)

Whenever participants drew upon their own knowledge, the group facilitator sought to establish the origin of the knowledge. These sources were subsequently re-introduced. Health professionals were asked to identify other ways in which information had been transmitted to them. Each source was explored in terms of its advantages and disadvantages as a channel of communication.

If any of the following training/knowledge resources was not mentioned spontaneously, they were introduced by the focus group moderator and group members were asked to rate their effectiveness:

- seminars/study days

- teaching packs

- leaflets

- training videos

- the Internet

- electronic mail (e-mail)

- a telephone helpline.

This particular element in the study allowed the moderator to question professional beliefs about the current and future information role of the HEA as a source of information, advice and support.

STUDY FINDINGS

Childhood diseases

Shared professional perceptions

There was a strong belief among health professionals that the immunisation programme has had a dramatic impact on the prevalence of infectious diseases. They identified two aspects:

- eradication – felt to be the case with smallpox and diphtheria;

- a far lower prevalence of certain other diseases, such as tetanus and whooping cough.

> We've got to educate the parents and make them aware that we don't actually see these diseases these days; and the reason why we don't see them is presumably because of the immunisation programme. *(GP, single profession group, North)*

There was also a view that this situation will continue only as long as uptake is maintained at a high level. Ironically, lower prevalence levels has led health professionals to admit that they find it difficult to recognise certain diseases:

> I struggle with measles. I struggle with rubella, too. *(GP, mixed group with practice nurses, Midlands)*

Discussants felt that parental knowledge about immunisation was derisory, that they would know the names of the diseases but little else. Parental knowledge was believed to be fragmented, for example, parents would be likely to think that diphtheria was a disease confined to history. Polio would be seen as a problem, but related only to 'the third world'. Older parents might have described their memories of people with withered limbs and callipers. Tetanus would be viewed as a disease arising from injuries such as thorns in the foot. Measles would be seen as no more serious than spots and a cough, and rubella would be associated with pregnancy. Whooping cough would be viewed as a mere bad cough, easily remedied by antibiotics and 'sorted out' in a few days, but meningitis *had* registered as serious. This was seen to stem from recent local outbreaks and the media coverage of such outbreaks.

However, it was thought that the heightened awareness of meningitis had some negative consequences as it could lead parents to assume wrongly that certain symptoms are always indicative of the disease:

> At the height of it last year, we must have been fielding calls of patients calling into the surgery for a quarter of the childhood population of this area that had a temperature, that outside of that time parents would have coped with in a common sense manner, but at that point their child must have meningitis because it was sweeping the area. *(Health visitor, mixed group with GPs, North)*

Professionals considered, moreover, that parents were unaware that meningitis occurred in several forms and that the Hib immunisation protected against only one form.

Reactions to the findings from the tracking studies and evaluation of the radio campaign

In 1996, 70% of mothers said that polio was a 'very serious' disease.

Health professionals expressed surprise at this, as polio is virtually no longer seen in the UK. They went on to speculate that the high figure might have been provoked by media coverage concerning adults who had, apparently, contracted polio from handling children:

> A couple of people have remembered it, because it was two years ago: two gentlemen picked up polio from changing dirty nappies. *(Health visitor, mixed group with GPs, North)*

The proportion of mothers rating whooping cough as 'very serious' has fallen from 76% in 1991 to 39% in 1996.

These figures did not cause any surprise. The discussants considered that parents are unlikely to have encountered whooping cough themselves and that they would be likely to associate it with symptoms not felt to be serious, such as a nasty cough. GPs in single profession groups further questioned whether it was important that *all* parents appreciate the seriousness of diseases such as polio or whooping cough, or whether this appreciation is important only in the case of defaulters.

Health professionals' information needs

Health professionals could see a need for two types of information, which might help them to persuade 'defaulters' to have their children immunised:

- the incidence of childhood diseases in their local area;
- graphic (and preferably visual) depictions of the implications of contracting these diseases, in order to alert reluctant parents to the seriousness of their consequences.

They expressed a wish to have information in a form which they could hand out to parents. Older health professionals felt that they would be able to supplement these with their own experience of childhood diseases.

Childhood immunisations

Shared professional perceptions

With only isolated exceptions, everyone interviewed felt that the uptake of immunisation in their practice was high. In some cases, however, this amounted to no more than an assertion that the rate of uptake is 'very good'. Where the uptake rate could be quoted, it was typically over 90% or over 95%, though this was sometimes qualified:

> I *think* we're over 90%. *(Practice nurse, single profession group, North)*

Sometimes only the rate for certain diseases could be quoted, or for certain age groups. There was confusion over whether the target level for the highest incentive is 90% or 95%. Predictably, uptake levels in inner-city areas were identified as lower. Here professionals considered there were higher priority health issues:

> We don't have enough time to deal with these people. We have enough other work to do ... It's not our priority, we don't bother. If the health visitor can do it, let them do it. *(GP, single profession group, Midlands)*

In determining parental knowledge of immunisations, health professionals identified two groups. One group of parents was seen to be affluent, well informed and well educated (although even members of this group are likely to believe that Hib protects against all forms of meningitis). They characterised the second group as having little idea of what immunisations were available. This group was said to comprise typically 'the lower social classes' and 'lower educational achievers'. Despite this latter group not knowing what immunisations were available, they were not anti-immunisation. They were perceived as people who firstly trusted their GP and secondly conformed to the normative pro-immunisation patterns and behaviours of neighbours and friends:

> I do feel that the majority go with the flow and just accept it as part of having a child, and this is what you do when you have had a baby. *(Practice nurse, mixed group with health visitors, North)*

Professionals identified two groups who 'defaulted'. One group was believed to consist of parents who had thought seriously about immunisation and then decided against it.

This group had come to the non-compliance position as a result of a combination of factors:

- concern about possible serious side effects;
- a preference for homeopathic treatment over conventional medicine;
- a dislike of all drugs and/or chemicals;
- an aversion to needles;
- ethical objections on religious grounds (for example, in the case of the rubella vaccine, they suspected that it was cultured on tissue from aborted foetuses).

The other group was thought to consist of parents who were not prepared to make sufficient effort to have their children immunised. It was felt that parents in the 'inefficient' category typically comprised several groups of people including parents of low socio-economic status. Such parents were said to have:

- other worries, so that health issues were not seen as a priority;
- a general lack of susceptibility to health-related advice;
- more immediate priorities, such as holidays, or social commitments;
- socially disorganised lives so that appointments are missed;
- literacy problems preventing them reading appointment cards in the first place;
- little incentive to turn up for any appointment;
- large families making it difficult to recall which children have already been vaccinated.

Typical social characteristics portrayed were:

- unemployed welfare-dependent demotivated parents;
- travellers (who were thought to expect immunisation to be taken to them);
- parents who live in 'out-lying areas', relying on inconvenient, infrequent public transport.

Reactions to the findings from the tracking studies and evaluation of the radio campaign

> One in five mothers still believes that Hib protects against all forms of meningitis.

Health professionals expressed no surprise when faced with this statement. Both practice nurses and health visitors claimed to be aware that mothers need to have the situation about Hib protection explained repeatedly, especially since they receive the initial information at a vulnerable moment, soon after the birth of their child.

> 26% of minority ethnic mothers were unable to name any immunisations spontaneously.

Again, this claim caused no surprise among participants. They linked this finding to a belief that there are specific groups of parents who have no idea what immunisations are available. They further suggested that the response could be attributed primarily to the predominance of first-generation, and hence less well-educated, mothers.

> Only 25% of minority ethnic mothers identified the correct explanation for what the Hib immunisation protects against (compared with 61% of white mothers).

This fact was accounted for by the difficulties entailed in communicating across language differences. Health professionals noted a scarcity of link workers to help them with such communication:

The link workers are available, but they are not exactly crawling out of the woodwork are they? Sometimes you have to do a visit or see somebody and the link worker is not there. You can maybe arrange for them to be there next time so you don't get caught like that again, but if you didn't know somebody was going to come to your session, they didn't speak English, they come with their invitation to cover for the vaccination, that counts as a prescription, basically. You give the vaccination, you give as much information as you can, but you can't guarantee that the are taking it all on board. *(Health visitor, mixed group with GPs and practice nurses, Midlands)*

Health professionals' information needs

Health professionals felt it important that they should receive adequate briefing *well in advance* of any changes to the immunisation programme. In their view, there is an inconsistency in practice. For example, they claimed that the introduction of the Hib vaccine was well organised, but that the introduction of the second MMR was not. They also indicated that information about the need for the second MMR did not reach practices before the immunisation was introduced or, in cases where it did, it did not always filter through to practice nurses and health visitors.

They also expressed concern that they still do not have sufficient information to counter questions about the possible link between MMR and Crohn's disease. Professionals also felt it to be the role of 'government' to raise public awareness about changes to the immunisation programme. This would help parents to understand why a new immunisation was important and dissipate fears about 'hidden agendas'. If such prior education had taken place parents would feel better informed *before* receiving notification from a practice.

Professionals considered television advertising an ideal medium for raising awareness. They also expressed a wish for a more structured approach for managing any fall-out from 'scare stories' (for example, the putative link between MMR and Crohn's disease). In this regard, they would ideally like three distinct types of information to combat each 'scare story':

- a warning in advance that such a story is about to break (if possible);

- an official response from government in the media, with a copy of the response circulated to themselves;

- suggestions as to how they might answer questions from parents who have seen or read the story.

Give us the information, the government line on it... give us the official statement. *(Health visitor, mixed group with practice nurses, North)*

In a similar way, they desired an 'official response' from government to soap-opera representations that they saw as 'misinformation' (for example, a dramatic episode of *Brookside* in which a mother thought that a local reaction to the meningitis vaccine was the symptom of something more serious):

> That was tremendous misinformation, again focusing on the one child. That woman, because he had a temperature, because he had actually a very good response to his immunisation, she said he could die from meningitis. That was a very irresponsible thing to say, because there are plenty of women out there who aren't very bright; they have got children, they see that and they think their child is immunised, he has got a temperature: meningitis. *(GP, mixed group with health visitors and practice nurses, Midlands)*

Health professionals additionally required advice about current arguments being put forward by 'anti-immunisation' lobbies, such as *JABS* or the *Society for Vaccine-Damaged Children*. They wanted access to official views about anti-immunisation arguments. As an example, some professionals had heard that *JABS* has claimed a link between the MMR immunisation and the development of autism.

A final requirement was for statistical data comparing the efficacy of homeopathy with conventional treatment to place health professionals in a better position when talking to mothers who have a preference for homeopathy. This was considered important given the increasing number of parents interested in alternative medical approaches. Indeed, one health visitor stated in the discussion that she regarded children who have received homeopathic treatment as 'covered'.

Side effects

Shared professional perceptions

Health professionals made distinctions about parental rights to information on side effects. They considered it appropriate to inform parents fully about common local reactions (such as rashes, temperature or restlessness) as opposed to rare serious side effects (such as anaphylactic shock, or brain damage). There was general agreement that parents should be given information about local reactions because parents would be most worried about what is going to happen in the hours immediately following the injection:

> They worry about what's going to happen tonight. They want to know how much Calpol they can give; they want to know whether the temperature is going to go up, and when it's going to, and what's going to happen and so on. And it's an immediate effect that they really are concerned about. *(GP, mixed group with health visitors, South)*

If parents were given the relevant information, they would know what to look for and how to treat it, and would be reassured that such reactions were normal.

There was, however, a consensus that serious side effects should *not* be discussed unless they are first raised by parents. Some GPs dismissed the matter of serious side effects altogether but most health professionals thought that to take the initiative in disclosing such information would create needless anxiety and turn parents 'against immunisation'. Nevertheless, there was a feeling that an increasing number of parents are seeking reassurance about serious side effects because of 'scare stories' in the press. When parents had raised the issue of serious side effects, health professionals claimed to have dealt with it in any combination of the following ways:

- pointing out in general terms that the risk of contracting the disease is much higher than the risk of suffering a serious side effect;

- pointing out that the link between vaccines and serious side effects has not been proven;

- reassuring parents that, if they control any rise in temperature their child suffers, this will prevent any convulsion;

- reading through the relevant section on adverse reactions in the 'green book' with parents.[1]

GPs in mixed profession groups claimed to feel more confidence about discussing safety in relation to certain vaccines like pertussis, which have been confirmed as safe through medical research. Such information is not yet available for MMR. They admitted that they tend to talk about the risk of serious side effects in general terms, in preference to citing statistics, either because they did not know what the statistics were or because the mere provision of statistics might give weight to the fact that a quantifiable risk exists. In some cases, they preferred to reason through analogy:

> I'm going to let you cross the road without looking once; on a quiet time, you're probably going to get across safely; but, if I make you do it one hundred times, you are probably going to get hit half a dozen times. *(GP, mixed group with health visitors, North)*

Practice nurses in single profession groups claimed that GPs can exert pressure on them to immunise children, even when those children might be slightly ill (e.g. have runny noses). In some cases, the nurses refuse to comply.

Health visitors in mixed profession groups expressed doubt with regard to government declarations about the safety of the MMR vaccine, in relation to Crohn's disease. Their doubts were intensified when they recalled similar assurances about BSE.

Reactions to the findings from the tracking studies and evaluation of the radio campaign

In 1996, 51% of mothers agreed with the attitude statement 'Doctors give sufficient information about the possible side effects of immunisation', and two in five disagreed.

Some GPs expressed surprise that the first figure was as high as 51%. This was owing to the health division of labour: there is a tendency for GPs to leave the discussion of side effects to health visitors and practice nurses and, as noted before, to talk about side effects only if the matter is first raised by parents. Health visitors, on the other hand, regarded 51% as low. They felt this was due to the time gap between the first home visit and when parents take their child to be immunised. Mothers could not *recall* being given information about side effects.

Health visitors also acknowledged that they did not dwell on the issue of side effects, asserting that they take the 'government line' as advocates of immunisation. In addition, they claimed to take upon themselves the task of judging how much information different parents can handle.

Health professionals' information needs

Health professionals from all three professions said that they wanted up-to-date statistics on the incidence of serious side effects for each immunisation. However, they also said that in practice they rarely used statistical material except, perhaps, to counter a particular media story.

The issue of choice

Shared professional perceptions

Practice nurses, health visitors and some GPs believed that parents have a basic right to decide whether or not to get their child immunised. Other GPs felt that immunisation should be mandatory, on public health grounds – for the sake of 'society as a whole':

> Nobody should be allowed into primary education unless they are immunised. *(GP, mixed group with practice nurses, Midlands)*

Some GPs felt so strongly about this that they would ask dissenting parents to de-register. Despite this minority opinion, most professionals believed that parents would 'like to think' that they had a choice about immunisation:

> In this country we have always been proud to have a free choice, and the freedom of the individual. *(Practice nurse, mixed group with health visitors, South)*

Other practice nurses disagreed and said that some parents would like it 'to be mandatory, so they don't have to make the decision'. Practice nurses and health visitors, however, also noted that parents may not, in fact, feel that they do have a choice because of the pressure exerted by GPs. This feeling could be linked to the successive reminders which are issued to defaulters. Paradoxically, some practice nurses are so conscious of not pressurising parents that they make a deliberate decision not to mention they have had their own children vaccinated.[2]

Reactions to the findings from the tracking studies and evaluation of the radio campaign

In 1996, 25% of mothers felt that they had no real choice about immunisation.

When faced with this finding, GPs speculated that mothers might feel they have no choice because 'society' as a whole (as opposed to health professionals) assumed immunisation is a good thing. However, they also recognised that their own procedures pre-empt informed consent.

Practice nurses in single profession groups tended to blame GPs for the 'no real choice' situation on the grounds that some GPs make mothers feel 'very guilty' for questioning immunisation. In addition they saw that opportunistic immunisation (that is, the unsolicited immunisation of a child at the same time as it is being treated for another condition) as 'coercing mothers' because they would lack sufficient time to form an individual view. Practice nurses thought that some parents did not read the information thus putting them at a disadvantage in making a choice.

On this issue, health visitors were more defensive. They claimed that they did provide parents with the necessary information. They also emphasised at each visit that parents can change their mind about immunisation. Therefore, if parents feel that they have not been given adequate information, it can only be because they failed to absorb it when it was given to them.

> 33% of minority ethnic mothers felt that they had no real choice about immunisation, and this rose to 50% in the Asian population.

The figures shown in this finding were again put down to the difficulties of communicating with minority ethnic mothers. One practice nurse, in a single profession group, claimed that ethnic mothers have complained about implicit racism, in terms of being forced into immunisation:

> Some of them are approached as in, you are in this country now, you do it our way. We have had women that have complained [about that]. *(Practice nurse, single profession group, Midlands)*

Practice nurses were also critical of the approach taken by some minority ethnic doctors. One spoke of 'an Asian doctor. And it was literally, just give it, just give it, just do it'!

The issue of consent

Shared professional perceptions

There are two stages to parental consent for immunisation. The first stage involves the signing of a form in which parents state that their child can be registered for immunisation. The second involves parental consent to the actual immunisation. No consistency of practice was found both within and across professions in relation to this crucial second stage. There were a set of competing and imprecise formulations.

- Consent to immunisation is implied if the parents have given consent for their child to be registered for immunisation. It was acknowledged by those health professionals who use this procedure that parents may not realise that they are consenting.

Those who accepted *implied consent*, on the whole, expressed no qualms about doing so. They felt that parents would not turn up if they did not want their child immunised. Furthermore, they argued that most medical treatment is given on the basis of implied consent.

> [Implied consent is when] the patient agrees to take medication, or agrees to an injection, or agrees to take advice, or agrees to be examined... They do it voluntarily, without objection. If I ask a patient to go on to the couch and get undressed, if he or she does that, then I take that as implied consent. If they had any questions or queries, then I would expect them to say so. *(GP, mixed group with practice nurses, North)*

Health professionals cited the 'green book' in support of the implied approach.

> Bringing a child for immunisation after an invitation to attend for this purpose may be viewed as acceptance that the child may be immunised.[1]

They also cited similar support in the nursing *Code of Conduct*.

GPs in single profession groups felt that it is the practice nurses who make 'an issue' out of consent. They considered that this arose because nurses wanted collective rather than individual responsibility. In other words, the practice as a whole to take ultimate responsibility rather than individuals were anything to go wrong. Some GPs who also believed that *they* themselves did not have to secure written consent before administering a vaccination but that practice nurses and health visitors *did* have to obtain such consent.

There was a feeling among GPs in mixed profession groups that the lack of any legal obligation to obtain written consent implied that there was less onus on them to ensure that parents fully understand immunisation.

Practice nurses in single profession groups expressed frustration that there was no uniformity across practices with regard to obtaining consent. They felt that such uniformity would lead to a greater feeling of security.

GPs and practice nurses made a distinction between 'consent' and 'informed consent':

> The definition of informed consent means that you have actually explained to the patient [sic] the implications of giving the vaccine, the benefits, the side effects, and [got] their agreement that it's the right thing to do. *(GP, single profession group, South)*

Both GPs and practice nurses were unsure about the nature of parents' actual understanding. They often assumed that the health visitor, as the first point of contact, had already provided the necessary information to make informed consent possible. This lack of clarity was not helped by the absence of any written protocol. Some GPs thought that true informed consent was simply impractical, implying as it does the acquisition of full knowledge by the parent.

**Reactions to the findings from the tracking studies and evaluation
of the radio campaign**

In 1996, 57% of mothers were directly asked for their consent prior to their
child being immunised; therefore, 43% were not.

There was speculation among health professionals that these figures arose
because they assumed that parents will have their child immunised, unless they
say otherwise. In any case, implied consent is *sufficient consent*. In addition, they
observed that the word 'consent' is unlikely to be used at any stage – parents are
more likely to be asked if they are 'happy' to have their child immunised:

> I usually say to them, "You know your first injection is due today, and are
> you happy with that?" And they just say, "Yes". And if they have got any
> queries, then address that then. *(GP, single profession group, South)*

Practice nurses who *did* claim to obtain verbal consent went on to stress how
important this is to themselves personally:

> It's part of your training to cover yourself. It's as much in your interest as it
> is in parents' interest. *(Practice nurse, single profession group, North)*

Assessing the delivery of the immunisation programme

Shared professional perceptions

Strengths
Overall, most participants considered the immunisation programme successful as
uptake was high. They viewed targets and incentives positively, seeing them as an
encouragement to pursue 'defaulters':

> The current arrangement for reimbursement that exists with targets has
> focused the general practitioner's attention on the issue of defaulters from
> vaccination, and I think that helps increase public awareness in that. *(GP,
> single profession group, North)*

They remarked on their use of tracking strategies in order to reduce the number
of 'defaulters' – repeat reminders, opportunistic immunisation (either in the
practice or in the home), going out to homes specifically to immunise the
children there.

Practice nurses alone raised the issue of the need for a written protocol. They
claimed that, in practices where such a protocol exists, it prevents confusion
about *what* information is given to parents, *who* gives that information, and
when that information is given.

Health visitors claimed that they are now routinely making efforts to explain to
parents what mild side effects can be expected after an immunisation. They
considered that this will reassure parents.

Weaknesses

Health professionals claimed that they are not always provided with sufficient information either to talk knowledgeably to parents about new vaccines (such as the second MMR) or to counter 'scare stories'. Sometimes information about new vaccines arrives too late.

There was also a fear expressed by all professions that targets might lead to some children being immunised at inappropriate times (such as when they have a fever or a runny nose). This might be the case if the family is prone to miss appointments.

Ineffective communication with minority ethnic family members was also cited as a problem. Professionals attribute this to several causes:

- language and communication difficulties;
- although link workers provide a useful means of communicating with ethnic mothers, they are not always available;
- although some health professionals do speak the relevant ethnic languages, they can experience technical difficulty with translation;
- although literature is published in ethnic languages, it may not always be available in the right language for a particular mother. Moreover, a patient may not be literate in his/her mother tongue.

Minority ethnic mothers may be second language speakers. Children may well be effective translators but there is likely to be technical language beyond their competence to translate. More problematically, there may well be sensitive topics which it can be inappropriate for a child to mediate between a professional and his/her mother:

> [The family] come along with a boy about ten, who is doing admirably, until you mention the word period – and then you're thinking, this is a bit of a no go area. *(GP, mixed group with health visitors, South)*

GPs in mixed profession groups felt that the delivery of the immunisation programme would be more effective if the government were to take more direct responsibility for communicating health messages. They thought explicit advertising addressed to parents would be far better than relying solely on health professionals.

These GPs also felt that the targets and incentives are set in such a way that they are more of an inducement to those who can readily obtain a high uptake. In addition, although the targets and incentives were perceived to contribute towards the successful delivery of the immunisation programme, they saw that the level of incentive was insufficient given the amount of paperwork involved. Moreover the extra work required was sometimes undermined because parents can be lost to a nearby 'competitor' such as a health clinic where free milk is distributed:

> I have nothing against the health authority immunising the children who are going for free milk, and things like that. But immediately they get immunised as well. Whereas I'm waiting in the surgery to get that child. That's another

thing that I don't like. Either the child should be immunised at the surgery, or the child should be immunised at the primary community health centre. You don't hold the carrot of free milk, and then immunise. Especially single practices like myself, where the number of children are ten, and nine come to me and if the tenth one doesn't come to me, I'm finished. I'm sunk. *(GP, mixed group with practice nurses, Midlands)*

GPs in single profession groups reiterated ideas that the targets and incentives are set in such a way that there is no inducement to go beyond 95% coverage.

They also expressed resentment at the perceived behaviour of health visitors within the immunisation programme. They saw them as acting independently, without communicating sufficiently with other health professionals about what advice they had given to mothers. They also claimed that health visitors often refused to give immunisations, even though they would be in a good position to immunise opportunistically. This was despite the fact that they are prepared to give other forms of injection:

> There's a requirement now that they have a certificate that they can vaccinate, like syringing ears, you know! It would take you two minutes to teach them, but [if] you've got to be certificated, it will take you three days. *(GP, single profession group, North)*

GPs in single-handed practices complained about having no health visitor assigned to their practice and as a consequence they had to bear the full responsibility for immunisation.

Practice nurses in mixed profession groups with GPs noted that the abbreviations for vaccinations which appear on parental appointment cards are generated by a computer and are already written in medical parlance – both factors combine to make it difficult for parents to understand:

> Because of the way the card is printed, they don't understand what is written on the card, because it's in computer briefing ... If it was the MMR, it would say 1 B MMR. That would be the booster programme. Also the 4-year-olds are having another injection at the same time, so it would say 1 B Dip Tet, 1 B Pol, and then 1 B MMR. They don't really understand what is written on the card. *(Practice nurse, mixed group with GPs and health visitors, Midlands)*

They felt, in addition, that parents might be put off by the prospect of a child having to be given two injections in the same visit (as is sometimes the case with the MMR vaccine).

Practice nurses in mixed groups with health visitors claimed to have experienced resentment from GPs, who are troubled by what they see as the expense of pursuing 'defaulters'. They felt that 'defaulters' are not always chased up because GPs were said to be 'cost-conscious'.

Practice nurses in sole profession groups expressed the feeling that GPs want to unload the full responsibility of delivering the immunisation programme onto them:

A lot of practice nurses have gone into running baby clinics on their own without any real training. I think that's happened a lot. *(Practice nurse, single profession group, North)*

This could lead, in turn, to GPs becoming 'blasé' about what information they provided for parents. They also claimed that inefficient record-keeping of immunisation histories has led to parents not receiving an appointment for certain immunisations.

The impracticalities of a clinic situation meant that there were problems in keeping children on the premises for the necessary 15 minutes after the injection has been performed – a procedure which is advised by certain consultants, but not the DoH. Practice nurses also expressed confusion about whether or not they should legally have a GP on the premises when they were administering vaccinations.

Practice nurses also commented on the lack of public information surrounding the necessity for a second MMR. They claimed that some parents who received an appointment for a second MMR assumed it was a mistake on the grounds that, having already had one MMR immunisation, their child was covered.

Health visitors in mixed profession groups felt that there was no consistent attitude among GPs towards certain issues, which made them uncertain about what stance to take when talking to parents. They too complained that certain practices do not have a well-organised appointment system.

When doing home visits, health visitors can feel a sense of isolation. They expressed concern that, when they are doing a home visit, there was nobody they could call for advice. This lack was keenly felt in rural practices.

They also expressed a reluctance to perform vaccinations in the home. They too believed that the presence of a GP was always required and they worried that they would not be able to deal with an adverse reaction.

Health visitors in sole profession groups expressed concern with immunisations which are to be given after the age of 1 year. At this stage, they are no longer doing domiciliary visits, so they worried that this loss of personal contact could lead to a corresponding drop in the uptake of immunisations scheduled for later. Those who are connected with practices which had no evening clinic said that it had proved difficult to reach children who required a second MMR because schools would not release children during the day.

Health visitors also expressed resentment towards other health professionals. They resented practice nurses, owing to their perceived over-cautious attitude towards giving immunisations and directed irritation to some GPs for their reluctance to give immunisations on the grounds that it would colour how children would feel about visiting them in future.

Reactions to the findings from the tracking studies and evaluation of the radio campaign

> In 1994, 18% of mothers who had accompanied their child on their last immunisation visit were dissatisfied with the outcome of the visit; this figure has now risen to 31%.

Health professionals from all professions expressed surprise at this finding, both at the fact that dissatisfaction is rising, and that the figure is as high as 31%. However, the figures tended to provoke defensiveness rather than concern. They rationalised this finding with three possibilities:

- long waiting times in clinics, where the atmosphere is stressful because of the number of people and the presence of crying children;

- the fact that, when a child suffered a mild side effect as a result of immunisation, mothers tend to forget that they have already been warned this might happen;

- mothers may not have been expecting the new MMR, and that it sometimes involved two injections at the same time.

> Minority ethnic mothers were more likely to report some level of dissatisfaction with their most recent immunisation experience (44% compared with 30% of non-ethnic mothers).

This finding caused no surprise except amongst health visitors. Most health professionals put minority ethnic mothers' dissatisfaction down to the difficulty of communication. Health visitors, however, claimed that minority ethnic mothers did not stand out as having any particular difficulties, accordingly 'they just flowed through'.

Information sources

Information sources previously or currently used

Health professionals spontaneously mentioned six which they were using, or had used in the past:

- the 'green book'[1]
- DoH circulars/letters from the CMO
- medical libraries
- study days
- telephone helplines
- distance learning courses.

The 'green book' (Immunisation against infectious diseases, DoH 1996)[1]

Health professionals described the green book as 'the Bible', in that it is likely to contain the answer to most questions from parents:

> It's a standard for everybody isn't it?... It's just your major reference source really, for suitability, contraindications and things like that [...] It's easy to understand, down to earth, practical and if it says it's all right in there, then it is all right. *(Practice nurses, single profession group, North)*

Health visitors were bothered by the fact that they did not always get their own personal copy. Practice nurses were divided as to whether it was suitable to read to, or with, parents.

Circulars from the DoH and letters from the CMO

These communications were felt to be a useful means of updating information contained within the green book; because they originated from official sources, professionals considered them to be reliable. GPs noted that these documents were sent to their home addresses, making it easier to distinguish them from 'junk mail'. The only reservation was about the length, which diluted their impact.

Medical libraries

Those who had used medical libraries claimed to have found them useful in providing information in response to a specific request:

> When I was told by the practice nurse about the Crohn's [disease] I said to one of the GPs, what is this, I haven't heard. And he said, oh, yes, there was an article way back in '95; perhaps we should get it from the library and have a look at it. Which we did. *(Health visitor, mixed group with practice nurses, South)*

Study days

Study days, organised either by the local community trust or by drug companies, were seen as being a good source of information provided that the speakers were respected by those attending. Professional credibility was crucial. In short, speakers should have given immunisations themselves and should know both the problems and the procedures in the attendees' local area(s). Opportunities for asking questions are important.

Some staff expressed reservations. Such events, for practical reasons, tend to occur on one specific day (unless part of a roadshow) which might make it impossible for people to attend. Furthermore, the need to set up study days well in advance makes it difficult for them to respond to immediate concerns. Health visitors and practice nurses both stated that there are circumstances which would prevent them from attending a study day. Health visitors claimed that they are forbidden by certain trusts to attend study days organised by drug companies as this would contravene their Code of Practice. Some practice nurses claimed that their GPs are reluctant to release them because cover, with a resultant financial cost, would be required. This point was echoed by GPs, who themselves do not attend study days for the same reason. Single-handed practitioners were especially reluctant, having to bear the cost of providing a locum.

Telephone helplines

These were felt by all health professionals to be a useful means of getting answers to questions, although there are a number of provisions which would have to be met:

- the helpline would have to be staffed outside office hours;

- information would have to be given on the spot (rather than looking up the answer);

- the person providing the information would have to be qualified and experienced in immunisation;

- GPs thought it would be best if the calls were recorded so that, in the event of something going wrong, there would be proof of what advice was given and the responsibility could thereby be 'passed back'.

Practice nurses in Leicestershire gave a positive account of their own informal helpline, run by a consultant.

Distance learning courses (GPs only)

These were felt to have the advantage that the professional is able to complete them in his or her own time, and they could count towards the five compulsory days of postgraduate training.

Professional responses to other potential information sources

After information sources had been raised spontaneously, a number of other possible sources were put forward by the researchers and discussed by health professionals.

Teaching packs

Health visitors regarded teaching packs as useful provided they are in a form which allows the information in them to be handed on subsequently to parents (for example, packs which contained a video). GPs and practice nurses, on the other hand, claimed that, in their experience, such packs tend to lie around the practice without being looked at.

Leaflets

These were thought to be useful only in relation to providing information for parents.

Training videos

In general, health professionals thought videos useful if directed to parents. They could be lent for use in the home or watched at home in the presence of a health visitor, or shown at the practice either in the waiting room, or at ante and postnatal classes. GPs and practice nurses thought that videos on their own would be unsuitable as a means of providing them with information, since videos require a dedicated amount of time for viewing. Nevertheless, practice nurses thought video viewing could form part of a study day if accompanied by an opportunity to ask questions. Health professionals were generally aware that videos take a long time to make but can become outdated quickly.

E-mail and the Internet

Although health professionals had heard of these, not all of them knew exactly what they were. Those who did know thought that they might be a quick means of relaying information, and that they would increasingly be seen as the accepted means of doing so (even for those who are working in practices where e-mail and the Internet are not currently in place). However, practices which had computers tend to use them for recording and storing information rather than communication. It was also thought that there could be no more guarantee that an e-mail will get through to the right person than a fax.

How professionals understood the current and potential role of the HEA

Health professionals tended to be confused by the term Health Education Authority. Some conceptualised it as a discrete body, while others failed to distinguish it from their regional health authority or from the DoH. Even those who thought the HEA was a discrete body had only a vague impression of it. However, they did tend to perceive its role as being to *inform the general public, rather than themselves*. This was because they were aware that certain pieces of literature they had been disseminating to their patients came from the HEA (e.g. *Birth to Five* book[3]). Health professionals thought that this perception of public orientation would persist in the future:

> I think health professionals will see them as health educators of the public rather than health educators of the health providers. *(GP, mixed group with health visitors, North)*

They saw the ideal role of the HEA involving the following:

- The *general promotion* of immunisation via:

  – advertising on television or in the press;

  – providing support materials for health professionals, such as leaflets for health visitors to leave with parents whom they visit or videos to be shown at home or in practices/clinics (these support materials in English and in relevant ethnic languages);

  – sending representatives into schools, in order to educate teenagers in advance about immunisation.

- The promotion of *specific immunisations* via the distribution of immunisation-specific literature, which can be sent out with appointments for that immunisation.

- The promulgation of the *rationale* behind new immunisations:

  – using the above dissemination methods;

  – setting up a telephone helpline to answer parents' questions.

The production of an *official response* to counter anti-immunisation messages. This was seen as particularly pertinent to the issue of minimising concerns about mild side effects, by issuing leaflets which could be handed out after each immunisation and which would explain what mild side effects might occur and how to treat them if they did.

In addition, health professionals naturally expected the HEA to *notify* them about, and to send them examples of, any direct communication which it has with the general public.

- Health professionals could also conceive of the HEA being a provider of information for *themselves*. They considered, however, that certain provisions would have to be met before this would be fully effective:

  – the HEA would have to do more to establish its credentials among health professionals, so that its authority would be recognised;

  – the HEA would have to ensure that it is a consistent source of the information required and that it did not duplicate information provided by another source (such as the DoH or local health promotion departments);

  – the information should be accessible.

RESEARCH CONCLUSIONS

Health professionals' understanding of parents

Research objective: to discover what health professionals understand to be the current perspective of parents with regard to immunisation.

Professionals in the study think that:

- although parents know the names of the diseases involved in the mass childhood immunisation programme, they know little else about them;

- parents divide into those who are well-informed and those who have no idea what immunisations are available;

- amongst non-immunisers, parents fall into two broad categories (see Table 5.2);

- parents want to feel that they have a choice about immunisation;

- parents' feelings about choice might be compromised through the pressure exerted by GPs and by the routinisation of clinic procedures.

Table 5.2 Groupings of non-immunisers

Parents who have decided against it, after serious consideration, for any combination of the following reasons:	Parents ('the feckless') who are unprepared to make the effort to have their child immunised, typically comprise:
concern about side effects	those of a lower socio-economic status
prefer homeopathic treatment	
dislike drugs/chemicals	single parents
fear needles	unemployed parents
	travellers
suspect that the rubella vaccine was cultured on aborted foetal tissue	those living in out-lying areas without any independent means of transport

Health professionals' reactions to findings about parents

Research objective: to compare and contrast what health professionals perceive spontaneously to be the current perspective of parents about immunisation, with their reaction to selective findings from the tracking studies and from the evaluation of the radio campaign.

Knowledge of diseases
When a high proportion of parents was reported as regarding a disease as 'very serious', this was greeted with surprise since health professionals were not aware that these diseases have registered on parents' perceptions (given their scarcity).

When the proportion is shown to be falling, this is attributed to the fact that parents would not have come across such diseases themselves.

Immunisation

Parents' confusion about the effectiveness of certain vaccines in protecting against all forms of a particular disease, specifically meningitis, is confirmed by health professionals' experience of having to explain this issue many times.

The inability of some minority ethnic mothers to name any immunisations matches the unprompted perceptions of health professionals that there are mothers who know almost nothing about immunisations. Similarly, the inability of some minority ethnic mothers to explain what certain immunisations protect against, matches the experience of health professionals. They claim that it was difficult to communicate successfully with such mothers given the language barrier and the lack of link workers.

Side effects

Some GPs were perplexed by the finding that as many as 51% of mothers feel that GPs give insufficient information about possible side effects. This was because they claimed that they were either disinclined or minimalist in raising such matters.

Choice

Health visitors and practice nurses concede that parents may feel that they have no choice about immunisation, confirmed in the finding that a high proportion of mothers reported such a feeling. GPs too conceded the above point but only after the tracking study results had been revealed.

Consent

The fact that some parents complained about lack of consent is clearly related to the different methods used by practices to assume rather than elicit consent.

Strengths and weaknesses of the delivery of the immunisation programme

The reported rising rate of dissatisfaction among mothers with the outcome of their immunisation visits was not anticipated by health professionals. The higher rate of dissatisfaction among minority ethnic mothers again tends to match the health professionals' experiences of communication difficulties with such parents (though even here, some still express surprise at the figures).

Health professionals' training needs

Research objective: to elicit what training needs health professionals themselves have with respect to successful delivery of the immunisation programme.

The following demands emerged:

- information about the incidence of diseases in their area, to pass on to defaulting parents;

- graphic and, where possible, visual descriptions of the implications of contracting each disease (again, to pass on to defaulting parents);

- active promotion, by government, of the fact that there are several forms of meningitis and that the Hib vaccine is effective against only one of these forms;

- an adequate briefing, well in advance, of any changes to the immunisation programme coupled with a high-profile public information campaign;

- prior warning, wherever possible, about 'scare stories' which are about to break in the media;

- official responses in the media from government to 'scare stories' and to television drama sequences which involve immunisation;

- advice on arguments currently propounded by anti-immunisation lobbies and official responses to these arguments;

- statistical data comparing the efficacy of homeopathy with that of conventional treatment;

- up-to-date statistics on the incidence of serious side effects for each immunisation, even though they may not be used;

- feedback from research conducted among parents, in order to help health professionals improve the services they provide.

The role of the HEA

Research objective: to identify both training needs and effective responses.

In meeting any of these needs, the HEA faces an immediate problem; health professionals tend to be confused about what the HEA is. Furthermore, health professionals who do envisage a role for the HEA, see it as informing the general public rather than themselves. Taken from this perspective, they visualise the HEA ideally as a direct point of contact with the public in four respects:

- promoting the benefit of immunisation through advertising and school visits;

- explaining new immunisations through advertising and via a helpline for parents;

- countering anti-immunisation news in the media;

- responding in the media to anti-immunisation drama sequences on television.

Some health professionals do perceive a role for the HEA in providing support materials for them. These resources could include the benefit of immunisation *per se*, the benefit of specific immunisations, and comments upon any mild side effects that may occur (and appropriate courses of action). Videos are cited as an ideal form and, to a lesser extent, leaflets.

If the HEA wishes to raise its profile amongst other health professionals, it would need to gain greater credibility. It would need to ensure that it offers consistent, accessible sources of information that are not duplicated elsewhere. Information health professionals would value includes:

- notification and examples of all communication with the general public;
- adequate briefing, well in advance, of any changes to the immunisation programme;
- warning of controversial material about to break in the media, and official counter-arguments to that material;
- feedback from research conducted among parents.

Information which health professionals cited as of value for their own professional development includes:

- brief circulars or letters;
- study days with 'respected' speakers;
- telephone helplines staffed by experienced personnel, who can supply information instantly;
- training videos which can be incorporated into a study day;
- in future, possibly e-mail and the Internet.

References

1. Department of Health. *Immunisation against infectious disease*. 1996. HMSO, London.
2. Gill, E., Sutton, S. 'Immunisation uptake: the role of parental attitudes', in Hey, V. (ed.) *Immunisation research: a summary volume*. 1998. HEA, London.
3. Health Education Authority. *Birth to five*. 1998. HEA, London.

4. Summary of factors affecting immunisation uptake levels

David Agbley and Helen Campbell

Communicable Disease and Immunisation Team
Health Promotion Branch
Department of Health

INTRODUCTION

Immunisation has led to the decline of many infectious childhood diseases, to the elimination of wild virus polio from many parts of the world and to the global eradication of smallpox. However, high levels of immunisation coverage need to be achieved and maintained for an immunisation programme to be successful. High coverage within a community serves to protect the minority of people who do not produce protective antibodies after receiving a vaccine and those who remain unimmunised; this is known as 'herd immunity'.

The World Health Organization's target for the European Region of 90% coverage adopted by the Government in 1985 has been exceeded and, as a result, a new national target of 95% coverage was introduced. It is the responsibility of each health authority to ensure that national targets are reached. In 1990 the DoH introduced strategies to promote higher uptake levels: GP target payments for primary vaccination and preschool boosters and the earlier, more condensed, schedule for primary immunisation, which made it easier for parents to complete. Children should now receive three doses of diphtheria, tetanus and pertussis (DTP), Hib and polio vaccines at 2, 3 and 4 months of age and one dose of measles, mumps and rubella (MMR) vaccine at 12–15 months of age. Further doses of diphtheria, tetanus, polio and MMR vaccines should be given at 3–5 years.

These changes have helped vaccine uptake in England continue to rise. In 1987-88, the uptake of diphtheria and measles vaccines by a child's second birthday were 87% and 76% respectively.[1] By 1995–96 coverage by the child's second birthday had increased to 96% for diphtheria vaccine and 92% for MMR vaccine.

Despite the high levels of uptake that are now being achieved nationally, there are still some areas and communities with relatively low coverage. It is important that these groups are identified so that they can be targeted in an appropriate way to encourage immunisation. Otherwise, pools of susceptible people will remain at risk of vaccine preventable disease outbreaks, with their associated morbidity and possible mortality.

This chapter examines vaccine coverage in England and, for these purposes, diphtheria vaccine uptake is used as a proxy measure for primary immunisation as recommended in the first year of life. MMR vaccine uptake is also considered, as a vaccine recommended at a slightly later age, in the second year of life. The available literature on different factors affecting immunisation uptake is reviewed.

IMMUNISATION COVERAGE

At national level

The national childhood immunisation programme in England is currently very successful. Figures on uptake by second birthday, up to December 1996, show that national coverage for diphtheria, tetanus and polio vaccines is at 96%, *Haemophilus influenzae* b (Hib) vaccine is at 95%, pertussis vaccine is at 94% and MMR vaccine is at 91%.[2]

At regional level

In the same period, all of the eight English regions achieved at least 90% coverage by first birthday for diphtheria vaccine. South and West Region was the only region to reach 95% uptake by this age. All the regions achieved 95% coverage by second birthday, except South Thames which reached 94% (see Figure 4.1).

Figure 4.1 Diphtheria vaccine coverage by first and second birthday: English regions, December 1996

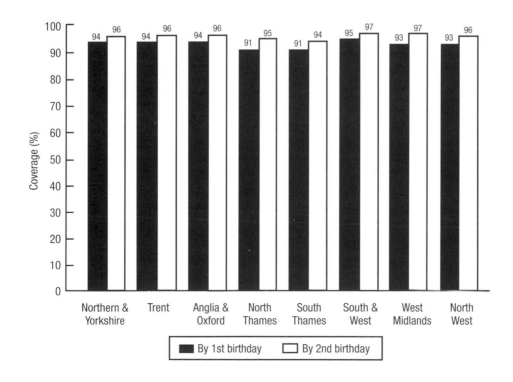

Figure 4.2 shows that seven of the eight regions achieved 90% coverage by second birthday for MMR vaccine, with South Thames reaching 88.0%. No region achieved 95% coverage.

Figure 4.2 MMR vaccine coverage by 2nd birthday: English regions, December 1996

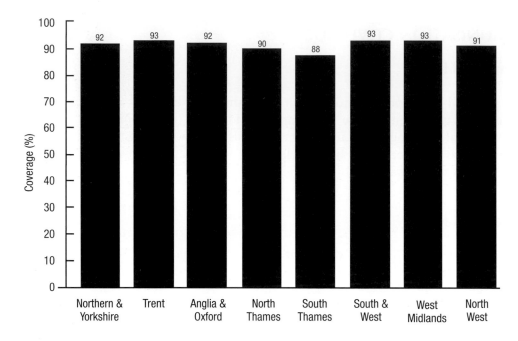

From these data it can be seen that both vaccines display a similar uptake profile across the regions, with South and West achieving the highest coverage and South Thames the lowest. In all regions MMR uptake is lower than diphtheria uptake.

At district level

The uptake levels achieved in December 1995 for diphtheria vaccine by second birthday for the 100 districts in England are summarised in Figure 4.3.[3] Only one district did not attain at least 90% coverage; 85% of districts achieved at least 95% uptake with the majority of these reaching 97% coverage or higher.

Figure 4.3 Diphtheria vaccine coverage by second birthday by districts in England: December 1995

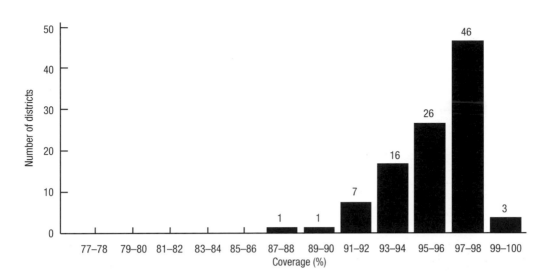

Information on MMR vaccine uptake by second birthday for the district level is summarised in Figure 4.4. MMR coverage is generally lower than that for diphtheria vaccine, and uptake levels are more widely spread; 35% of districts did not attain more than 90% coverage. One district had a very poor uptake of 77%. Although many districts (42%) reached 91-94% uptake levels, and 23% of districts achieved at least 95% coverage – none were higher than 96%.

Figure 4.4 MMR vaccine coverage by second birthday by districts in England: December 1995

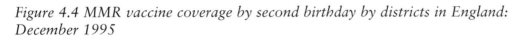

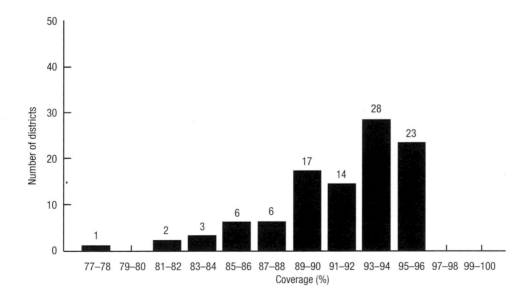

Table 4.1 summarises the district immunisation uptake for diphtheria and MMR vaccine by second birthday for each region. This shows that all of the districts in the South and West Region achieved at least 95% uptake for diphtheria and also had the best performance for MMR uptake. Districts in the South Thames Region were the poorest achievers overall, and had the widest range of uptake levels for both vaccines.

Table 4.1 Summary of district immunisation uptake by second birthday for each region: England, December 1995

Region	No. of districts	Diphtheria uptake by 2nd birthday		MMR uptake by 2nd birthday	
		Average % (range)	No. reaching 95%	Average % (range)	No. reaching 95%
Anglia and Oxford	9	96 (91–99)	7	93 (84–96)	5
North Thames	14	95 (90–97)	11	90 (82–95)	2
South Thames	12	94 (87–99)	5	89 (77–95)	1
South and West	12	97 (96–98)	12	94 (90–96)	3
West Midlands	13	96 (93–98)	11	93 (87–96)	4
North West	16	96 (91–98)	13	91 (85–93)	0
Northern and Yorkshire	13	95 (91–99)	8	92 (89–96)	3
Trent	11	96 (93–98)	8	93 (88–96)	5

The difference between uptake levels for diphtheria and MMR vaccines suggests that distinct factors may affect coverage at different ages and/or for different antigens. Vaccine uptake levels for diphtheria by first birthday and MMR by second birthday, which have similar reporting time frames, are consistently higher for diphtheria in every region, although only by a maximum of two percentage points. This suggests that the observed differences cannot be explained entirely by the reporting time period for providing these data.

THE CHILDHOOD IMMUNISATION INFORMATION SYSTEM

Immunisation rates are calculated from the local Child Health System (CHS) database.[2] This system usually produces an appointment invitation for each child living in the area based on the national immunisation schedule and the child's age. The invitation is then either sent directly to the parents or to the centre where the immunisation is going to be carried out for the appointment to be scheduled.[4] Following the allotted appointment, information on the completion of immunisation should be fed back to the child health computing system.

The importance of this process has been illustrated by a study in the London Borough of Greenwich which looked predominantly at the capture of immunisation data and improvements in these systems.[5] In November 1990 the immunisation uptake in Greenwich was less than 65% for pertussis vaccine and less than 70% for diphtheria and measles vaccines. The low recorded uptake rates resulted in low morale, frustration and general unhappiness amongst field staff.

At that time three main problems were identified: poor return rates and late inaccurate returns; backlogs of data input; no data validation. Uptake was increased to more than 80% for all antigens after the inputting backlog was cleared, bad return rates and late returns were addressed and the data was validated. From 1992 steps were taken to secure the information flow, and close the audit loop by:

- computerised scheduling of immunisations for all clinics;

- sending quarterly DTP/polio and MMR defaulter lists to geographical bases;

- returning turn around documents to GPs for amendment of their records;

- visiting GPs to secure information flow and to create a deeper understanding of the total system – how the CHS, FHSA and the GPs' systems interact for the delivery of childhood immunisation and the collection of immunisation statistics;

- the rolling introduction of computerised scheduling for GPs;

- attachment/alignment of health visitors to GP practices whilst retaining some geographical responsibilities for children not registered with a GP.

Poor communication channels between some GPs and the CHS were identified as the last weak link in the system. This was considered to be because a different computer system is used for payment of GPs and there was little or no incentive for GPs to supply immunisation data separately to the CHS.

Once these issues were addressed the uptake in Greenwich then exceeded 90% for both diphtheria and pertussis.

THE EFFECT OF POPULATION CHARACTERISTICS

Mobile population

The majority of districts contain some families that are highly mobile. These families include unemployed single parents, overseas parents, Gypsy parents and New Age Traveller parents, who tend to live in temporary accommodation. As these people are extremely difficult to trace, immunisation appointments are much less likely to reach them.[6] Some of the children of these families may have been vaccinated by a doctor in a different district, but are registered by the CHS as not immunised. This tends to affect the figures for immunisation uptake levels, with underestimates of true coverage rates being recorded. It has been suggested that other barriers to uptake of immunisation for Travellers/Gypsies include discrimination from doctors, enforced mobility, illiteracy and the absence of postal addresses for recall.[7]

Feder *et al.* carried out a study in East London from 1988 to 1990 which looked at primary immunisation uptake for children of Traveller/Gypsy families living in an inner city area.[7] They found that the completion rate for primary immunisation for these children was low compared with the local settled population, which was made up of many ethnic groups with a high proportion of low income and single parent families. The lowest rate was for pertussis and measles vaccines, where there was a large difference between the two populations.

However, over two-thirds of Traveller/Gypsy children had had their first diphtheria/tetanus and poliomyelitis vaccines, underlining the fact that these parents had no objections to vaccines in principle. Involuntary mobility, lack of a GP and lack of information about community health services were cited as factors which reduce the access of Travellers/Gypsies to immunisation.

The different health needs of Traveller/Gypsy families have been recognised in some health authorities, and poor immunisation uptake is targeted in some areas with the provision of mobile clinics.[8] In Oxfordshire a nursing post to cover home immunisation was established in 1984 and expanded to cover wider health issues in 1986. Parent-held Child Health Records were also introduced and found to be most useful, in particular for continuity of care for Traveller/Gypsy families.

The problem of immunisation of children from Traveller/Gypsy families not being recorded on the CHS has been addressed in Oxfordshire by assigning codes to these children so that they are automatically identified as a separate group (personal communication). The immunisation coordinator then has the responsibility for validating their records.

Ethnicity

A number of studies have identified differences in the rate of uptake among children of different ethnic origins. A study in Bradford used the 1980 birth cohort to determine whether there were differences among ethnic groups in the utilisation of the NHS, as reflected in the uptake of immunisation which should be offered to all children.[9] This study suggested that there are differences among different ethnic groups (see Table 4.2); Asian people had the highest uptake for both antigens, and black people of mixed parentage registered the lowest uptake. It is important to note, however, that the sizes of the ethnic groups were very different. This makes it difficult to draw any firm conclusions. The study suggested that the differences in uptake were likely to be due to a mixture of factors relating to the NHS, the community and the local environment.

Table 4.2 Immunisation uptake by 27 months for six ethnic groups in Bradford health district: 1980[9]

Antigen	Caucasian* (n=3545)	Indian (n=343)	Pakis-tani (n=1396)	Black – mixed parentage (n=48)	West Indian (n=35)	Bangla-deshi (n=37)	Asian – mixed parentage (n=54)
Diphtheria	80.0	95.5	85.7	64.5	71.4	78.4	81.5
Pertussis	47.6	78.7	69.4	29.2	48.1	54.1	47.6

* Caucasian group was used as standard population for all antigens

Bhopal and Samim conducted a retrospective cohort study of immunisation uptake among Asian children born in Glasgow in 1983.[10] Children of Asian origin were identified by name and categorised by religion and compared to children with European names. Their study showed that children with Asian names were better immunised than their non-Asian counterparts. The difference in uptake between the Sikh children and their non-Asian counterparts for diphtheria, pertussis and measles were 5, 17 and 10 percentage points respectively.

These differences have not yet been explained, but high uptake of immunisation among Asian people is not unique to Bradford and Glasgow.[8] High uptake within the Asian community may be due to traditional systems of medicine and folk medicine, which focus on preventing rather than curing disease, and fear of infectious diseases resulting from experiences in the Indian subcontinent. Bhopal and Samim suggested that Asian parents, due to their poorer knowledge of English, were less sensitive to the media's portrayal of vaccination and to professional uncertainty.[9]

It is difficult to determine whether there are still differences in uptake in ethnic minority groups and what these differences are, as little information is available. Studies have indicated that girls in India have poorer access to health services than boys: in Bombay boys have immunisation rates 16% higher than girls.[11] However, a study based in Newcastle found no significant difference in immunisation uptake by gender, for South Asian or European children. This study also supported the finding that immunisation rates are higher in South Asian populations when compared to European children.[11]

Social and family factors

The 1989 Peckham report showed immunisation uptake to vary with socio-economic groups (see Table 4.3[12]). The difference in uptake between social groups I and II and social groups IV and V for measles and pertussis was 8 percentage points for both antigens.

Table 4.3 Socio-economic group and immunisation uptake[12]

Social group	number	% measles uptake	% pertussis uptake
I and II (professional/managerial)	1041	90	87
III (clerical/skilled manual)	1475	86	85
IV and V (partly skilled/unskilled)	555	82	79
Other (student, unemployed)	267	75	77

The presence of older siblings and of chronically ill children in families from lower socio-economic groups was also found to be strongly associated with lower uptake.[12] In such situations immunisation appointments can become a lower priority. The difference in uptake for measles and pertussis was 16 and 17 percentage points respectively for families with a chronically ill child compared to those without. The same study showed that the number of siblings in a family can affect immunisation uptake. The difference in uptake between 'only child' and two or more older siblings for measles and pertussis was 14 and 13 percentage points respectively. Another study also found that birth order also influenced uptake – MMR vaccination was significantly lower in third or later born children. And children in single parent families have been found to have a lower uptake of MMR vaccine than children in two parent families.[6]

Residential area

'Inner city' status has been identified by a number of studies as a factor contributing to lower uptake. Li and Taylor showed that MMR uptake tends to be lower in inner cities compared to urban areas (see table 4.4).[6] The authors believed that the main cause of lower uptake in the inner cities was the composition of the population (for instance, a high proportion of families were from minority ethnic groups, in lower socio-economic groups, with large numbers of children) rather than the 'inner city' status itself.

Table 4.4 Uptake rates of MMR vaccine in ten districts in N.E. Thames and N.W.Thames[6]

	Inner city district						Rural or urban district				Overall
	1	2	3	4	5	6	7	8	9	10	
Uptake rate (%)	81	68	81	76	74	72	87	91	87	81	81

One study, based in Northumberland, measured immunisation uptake in cohorts of children before and after a number of interventions, designed to improve uptake, had been introduced.[13] The children were classified by residential area and allocated one of five groups from the most deprived to most affluent area, using Townsend deprivation scores. In sequential study periods, overall uptake increased substantially in every study group. However, the odds of a child being immunised against pertussis and diphtheria in the most affluent area was more than twice that in the most deprived area, even after the intervention. Inequalities in measles uptake also persisted after intervention. This study suggested that even after successful interventions to improve immunisation uptake in all children, inequalities may persist.

A possible relationship between Jarman score (an indicator of socio-economic deprivation) and immunisation uptake has been investigated. The Jarman score is the weighted total of eight transformed and standardised census variables:[14] These are:

- elderly living alone;

- children under 5 years;

- resident in 'lone parent' household;

- resident in household with a head of household in the unskilled socio-economic group;

- unemployed as a percentage of economically active;

- resident in overcrowded household, that is, more than one person per room;

- residents who have changed address in the previous year as a percentage of total residents;

- resident in household headed by a person born in the New Commonwealth.

The OPCS 1991 Census data were used to plot a graph of Jarman score against diphtheria and MMR vaccine uptake by second birthday using health authority data published in the 1995–96 NHS Performance Guide (see Appendix 1).[3,15]

Analysis of the correlation between Jarman score and immunisation uptake provides some evidence of a small but significant fall in immunisation uptake as deprivation increases (for diphtheria Rho= -0.28, P=0.005; for MMR Rho= -0.32, P=0.002).

Since the Jarman score is the sum of eight variables (listed above) looking at the combined Jarman score may mask a strong relationship with one of these factors. Further analysis using multiple regression could be used to look for a link between uptake and one or more of these factors, if the components of each score were available.

SERVICE PROVISION

Reasons suggested for failure to reach immunisation targets include both characteristics of the targeted population and the services provided. The low priority attributed to immunisation services in resource allocation, insufficient training of health professionals and division of responsibility for carrying out immunisation between GPs and community health services have been implicated in poor immunisation rates.[16]

In areas where immunisation clinics or centres are not readily accessible due to poor transport systems and inconvenient opening times (as in areas where vaccination is administered at community health clinics), this may result in poor uptake.[17]

General practices have been found to do better than community health clinics in providing primary immunisation for the following reasons:

- financial encouragement for GPs to meet the target for immunisation;
- more efficient communication between GPs and families with more effective consultation on immunisation;
- more flexible and convenient immunisation session times in general practice, especially for working parents or parents with other children.

PARENTAL REFUSAL TO HAVE CHILDREN IMMUNISED

'Anti-immunisation' groups have existed since the invention of immunisation. These groups are producing an expanding body of literature in the form of newsletters, books, articles in fringe journals and videos.[18] Their misgivings rest on three arguments:

- The success of immunisation in eliminating infectious disease is widely exaggerated and inaccurately reported;
- the seriousness of short-term effects has been played down;
- long-term damage to health from vaccines has never been properly investigated but may prove to be far-reaching.[19]

There are anecdotal reports that an increasing number of educated parents who have access to this literature refuse immunisation because they believe health professionals are presenting only one side of the story.

Elliman has suggested that these 'doubters' have often read widely in this non-medical literature and come prepared with a number of references to back up their concerns.[18] He, therefore, emphasises the need for all health professionals to have good current knowledge of the effectiveness of vaccination, levels and seriousness of infectious disease and adverse reactions, in order to be able to debate with parents.

An increasing interest in alternative and complementary therapies in recent years, especially in homeopathy, has also resulted in some parents refusing immunisation. Homeopathy is a system of treatment based on the principle that substances which cause symptoms can also be used to cure them. The Society of Homeopathy, the representative body of lay homeopaths, does not have an official policy on immunisation, but it considers that parents should have access to enough information to allow them to make an informed decision. Medically qualified practitioners, who are represented by the Faculty of Homeopathy, support immunisation with conventional vaccines.

In 1994, Simpson *et al.* studied why some parents in Bath refused to have their children immunised. They found that over a fifth of parents refusing immunisation cited homeopathy as a reason for not immunising their children.[19] A further article reported that South Essex Health Authority was forced to intervene after doctors complained that homeopaths were encouraging parents to refuse immunisation for their children.[21] The Health Authority sent a letter to all GPs urging them to show non-consenting parents a paper, 'Enough nonsense on immunisation', produced by the Faculty of Homeopathy which outlined the Faculty's support for immunisation.[22] The success of this strategy was not reported.

Simpson *et al.* also found that religious beliefs accounted for 16% of the refusals in their study.[20] Lack of support for immunisation was present in the beliefs of the Christian Science Church, but a brief survey of other religious groups showed that they were all broadly in favour of immunisation. The authors concluded that people (other than Christian Scientists) who refuse immunisation on religious grounds do so through their own interpretation.

THE INFLUENCE OF HEALTH CARE PROFESSIONALS

The attitude and behaviour of all health professionals has a major influence on parental decision-making about vaccination. One of the factors determining high uptake of immunisation is GPs' knowledge about the contraindications to immunisation. In the National Immunisation Study, GPs' knowledge on contraindications was found to be associated with the level of uptake in their practice.[12] No such relationship between health visitors' knowledge and vaccine uptake was found. The level of health professionals' knowledge about contraindications may reflect their wider knowledge of all immunisation.

Interventions by health professionals in cases of persistent non-attendance have improved immunisation uptake levels. Crittenden and Rao studied the impact of the intervention of the immunisation coordinator on immunisation uptake in Essex in 1994: 93 children whose parents had not responded to repeated invitations for different immunisations, were identified.[23] Eleven cases were lost to follow-up: the families of ten children had moved out of the area, and one child had died. 82 children fell within the parameters of the study. All these children were referred to the immunisation coordinator and 58 were successfully vaccinated. As a result of the intervention by the immunisation coordinator, coupled with the efforts of GPs and the primary health care team, the uptake increased from 87% to 90% for the booster DT/polio immunisations within a year.

In 1990, health visitors based at a practice, situated in an area of acknowledged social deprivation in Cardiff, were concerned about the low uptake in childhood immunisations. Over a period of 12 months they developed a joint immunisation protocol in collaboration with the primary health care team to enable improved uptake.[24] The protocol addressed a number of issues including the identification of families in need of extra support, modifications to health authority policy to allow health visitors to perform immunisation on a home and opportunistic basis after appropriate training, and standardised professional advice. Over a three-month pilot period, 23 children were identified as failing to complete the primary course of immunisation. Of these children, 74% were immunised by the health visitor during surgery-based opportunities and 26% were immunised at home. The subsequent introduction of the immunisation protocol led to significant improvements in primary immunisation uptake; the uptake rate, which had been 72%, was now consistently over 90%.

CONFIDENCE IN DIFFERENT VACCINES

Parental beliefs about different vaccines appears to influence uptake. A major finding in the 1993 study by Li and Taylor was that uptake of MMR vaccination was strongly predicted by uptake of DTP immunisation.[12] A study in 1993 by Barrett and Ramsay[25] found that those factors associated with low uptake for MMR vaccine in Li and Taylor's study, were similar to those affecting diphtheria and tetanus uptake.[13]

Peckham *et al.* (1989) found that parents considered measles to be more infectious than pertussis, but considered pertussis to be a more serious disease.[12] They were less confident about the safety of pertussis vaccine. 64% cited risks attached to pertussis vaccine compared with 25% for measles vaccine. Thirty-eight per cent of respondents specified brain damage as a complication of pertussis vaccine thus demonstrating persisting fears about its safety.

Information on coverage at regional and district level, as described on pages 83–6, suggests that MMR uptake may currently be influenced by different factors to those affecting DTP, polio and Hib uptake. High media interest in possible adverse reactions following the measles/rubella campaign in November 1994, in which 8 million school children were immunised, may have increased parental concerns about the safety of MMR vaccine. Adverse publicity concerning the safety of MMR vaccine has appeared sporadically in the media since that time. Coverage levels for this vaccine have declined marginally since November 1994 with fewer districts achieving 95% uptake.[26]

SIZE OF GP PRACTICE

Studies have shown that where there is a team approach and a single individual with responsibility for the immunisation programme, in practices with more than one GP, then vaccine coverage is better.[16] In single-handed practices where there are efficient managerial staff, immunisation uptake levels can be as high as in the multi-practice.

The possible relationship between GP practice size and immunisation uptake was investigated by using the General Medical Practitioner census data for October 1995 to calculate the average number of GPs per practice for each health authority. This average was then plotted against diphtheria and MMR vaccine uptake by second birthday using health authority data published in the 1995–96 NHS Performance Guide (see Appendix 2).

Analysis of the correlation between average GP practice size and immunisation uptake using Spearman's Rank method provides some evidence of a small but significant increase in immunisation uptake with increasing average practice size (for diphtheria Rho=0.24, P=0.02, for MMR Rho=0.3, P=0.001). However, some single-handed practices do achieve high uptake and, undoubtedly, some large practices do not.

SUMMARY

A number of studies have examined different factors in relation to vaccine uptake. National immunisation coverage has increased notably in recent years and it seems likely that the significance of at least some of the factors affecting uptake has changed in that time. Therefore, further research is now required to provide evidence of the various contributory factors.

It appears that there are both practical and educational barriers to immunisation. For some groups the barriers to having children immunised may be entirely due to the logistics of accessing health services, as with mobile families, parents with one or more other children and those with a child who is chronically ill. In some areas these practical problems have been addressed by introducing home and opportunistic immunisation. Intervention by the immunisation coordinator, who takes direct responsibility for follow-up of children who have not completed immunisation or for those that belong to groups with low uptake, has been shown to be helpful. In the first instance, it is important to ensure that children who have not been appropriately immunised are identified. This requires accurate and up-to-date record keeping which is facilitated by effective information feedback mechanisms.

Parents are increasingly demanding more information about immunisation and, in particular, vaccine safety. Thus, it is important for health professionals to have sufficient knowledge about immunisation to address sophisticated objections to vaccines from educated parents. Information that details the support that religious groups and homeopaths have given in favour of immunisation may be useful to counter refusal to have a child immunised on such grounds.

Health visitors are well placed to deliver early information on immunisation to parents. It may be possible to utilise both health visitors and practice nurses more effectively to discuss parental concerns about vaccines. Groups that it may be possible to encourage through delivery of targeted information include:

1. Parents with concerns about immunisation in general and vaccine safety in particular – easily accessible, detailed information about the benefits and risks of immunisation for parents is required locally and parents need to be aware of its existence.

2. Parents with one or more older children and those with children who are chronically ill – health visitors or GP practices may be able to identify these groups of children who do not present for immunisation.

3. Parents whose children have not completed the primary course of DTP, polio and Hib at the time their MMR immunisation is due – the CHS or GP practice should be able to identify these children.

4. Health professionals who immunise children – appropriate training material may be helpful to increase knowledge of all vaccines, side effects and contraindications and the diseases that are being targeted.

The first in a series of detailed immunisation fact sheets[27] aimed at addressing the needs of groups 1 and 4 is now available.

Whilst the observed association between increasing GP practice size and increasing MMR vaccine uptake is interesting, it is preliminary. The observation hides the fact that some single practices do achieve very high uptake levels. An association between Jarman score and immunisation uptake level was identified, and one or more of the criteria that contribute to the overall Jarman score may be important in influencing immunisation uptake. Further study would be needed to identify any such link.

It would be valuable to gather additional current information about a number of factors that have been identified in the past as having an effect on uptake, such as ethnic group, socio-economic group and mobile populations. Understanding why higher levels of uptake were found in some Asian communities, for example, may be helpful in developing strategies to encourage other groups within the population to participate in immunisation programmes. Concerted action in districts where low uptake is observed and active encouragement and support for GPs achieving relatively low levels of uptake, can help increase coverage locally and should consequently raise uptake levels for the whole country.

References

1. Department of Health Statistics Division. *Vaccination and immunisation: summary information for 1994–95*. 1997. Government Statistical Service.

2. Public Health Laboratory Service. *Communicable Disease Report Weekly*, March 1997; 7(13): 111–12.

3. NHS Executive. *The NHS Performance Guide 1995–96*. Department of Health. June 1996.

4. Li J., Taylor, B. 'Comparison of immunisation rates in general practice and child health clinics', *British Medical Journal*, 1991; 303: 1035-8.

5. McCavanagh, C. A paper on the successful capture of childhood immunisation information in the London Borough of Greenwich. 1994. Unpublished.

6. Li, J., Taylor, B. ' Factors affecting uptake of measles, mumps, and rubella', *British Medical Journal*, 1993; 307: 168–71

7. Feder, S., Vaclavik, T., Streetly, A. 'Traveller Gypsies and childhood immunisation: a study in East London', *British Journal of General Practice*, 1993; 43: 281–4.

8. Moreton, J. 'Immunisation of travellers in Oxfordshire', *Nursing* 1987, 19.

9. Baker, M.R., Bandaranayake, R., Schweiger, M. 'Differences in rate of immunisation among ethnic groups', *British Medical Journal*, 1984; 288: 1075–8.

10. Bhopal, R.S., Samim, A. K. 'Immunisation uptake of Glasgow Asian children: paradoxical benefit of communication barriers', *Community Medicine*, 1988; 10: 215–20.

11. Martineau, A., White, M., Bhopal, R. 'No sex differences in immunisation rates of British South Asian children: the effect of migration?' *British Medical Journal*, 1997; 314: 642–3.

12. Peckham, C., Bedford, H., Ades, A., Senturin, Y. *National immunisation study: factors influencing immunisation uptake in childhood.* 1989. Action Research for the Crippled Child, Horsham.

13. Reading, R. *et al.* 'Do interventions that improve immunisation uptake also reduce social inequalities in uptake?' *British Medical Journal*, 1994; 308: 1142–4.

14. British Market Research Bureau. *The uptake of pre-school immunisation in England.* 1989.

15. OPCS. Underprivileged area score for Regional and District Health Authority, 1991 Census.

16. Jefferies, S., McShane, S., Oerton, J., Victor, C. 'Low immunisation uptake rates in an inner-city health district: fact or fiction', *Journal of Public Health Medicine*, 1991; 13(4): 312–17

17. Baxter, D. N. 'Improving immunisation uptake in the United Kingdom', *Public Health* 1990; 104: 267–74.

18. Elliman, D. Immunisation – the doubters. 3 December, 1995.

19. Bedford, H., Maceoin, D. 'The immunisation debate', *Childright*, 1992; 83: 11–15.

20. Simpson, N., Lenton, S., Randall 'Parental refusal to have children immunised: extent and reasons', *British Medical Journal*, 1995; 210–227

21. Catherall, S. 'Homeopaths in jabs refusal row', *Doctor*, January 1996; 14

22. Editorial. 'Enough nonsense on immunisation,' *British Homeopathic Journal*, 1990; 79: 198–200.

23. Public Health Laboratory Service. Crittenden, P., Rao, M. *Communicable Disease Report.* 1994; 4(7): R70–R81.

24. Clark, J., Day, J., Howe, E., Williams, P. 'Developing an immunisation protocol for the primary health care team', *Health Visitor*, 1995; 68(5): 195–8.

25. Barrett, A., Ramsay, M. 'Improving uptake of immunisation', *British Medical Journal*, 1993; 307: 681.

26. Public Health Laboratory Service. *Communicable Disease Report.* 1996; 6(30): 262.

27. Health Education Authority and Department of Health. *Immunisation factsheets.* 1998. HEA, London.

Appendix 1

Correlation between Jarman score and diphtheria vaccine uptake
by health authority

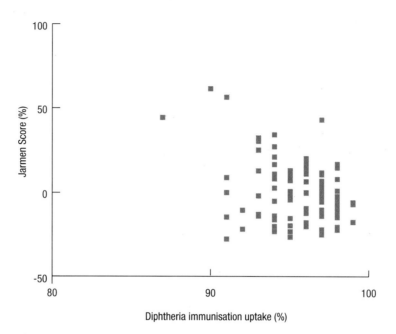

Correlation between Jarman score and MMR vaccine uptake
by health authority

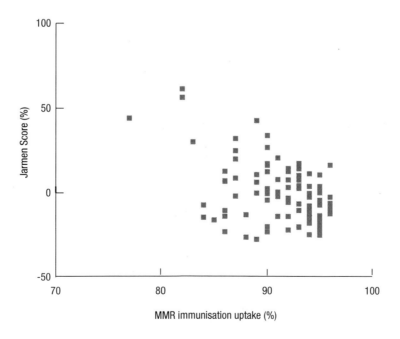

Appendix 2

Correlation between GP practice size and MMR vaccine uptake by health authority

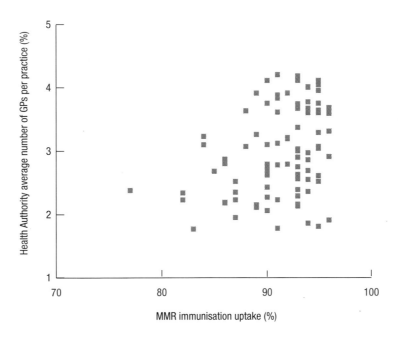

Correlation between GP practice size and diphtheria vaccine uptake by health authority

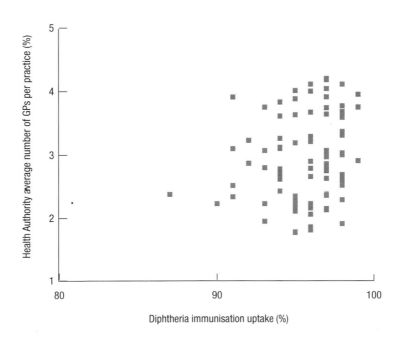